REARING
THE LAYING
PULLET

A FARMERS WEEKLY PAPERBACK

D1352838

Silcock Research does it again !

Following upon the introduction of the celebrated H.Y.-L.C. Plan for milk producers and the S3P Plan for pig keepers, Silcocks now announce THE MILLMOOR* PLAN

The entirely new concept in poultry nutrition

Research workers at Millmoor have found that different rations are needed by the light bodied birds on the one hand and the heavier birds on the other, not only during lay, but right from shell.

Now Silcocks-and only Silcocks-offer a completely separate range of foods giving each type of bird the precise nutrients she needs at every stage from shell onwards.

The result . . . More chicks at even lower cost. Higher Production. Larger egg size. Better shelling. Deeper yolk colour.

Telephone or write direct to Liverpool for your copy of the brochure describing the new Millmoor Foods.

*Millmoor is the name of the Silcock Poultry Research Establishment, one of the largest of its kind in Europe.

R. Silcock & Sons Ltd., Stanley Hall, Liverpool 3

CONTENTS

CONTRIBUTORS

Dr. C. Horton-Smith, Animal Health Trust, Houghton Poultry Research Station, Hunts.

Dr. D. W. B. Sainsbury, School of Veterinary Medicine, Cambridge.

T. R. Morris, Reading University

Huntly Watson (F. & G. Sykes Ltd.)

F. & G. Sykes, Ltd.

A. K. Smith

Staff of *The Farmers Weekly*

INTRODUCTION

The first consideration in getting high egg production is choice of strain. Next, and no less important, is efficient rearing. There are many methods of rearing, all depending for success on conscientious, sympathetic understanding of a bird's needs. Mere technical qualifications cannot replace human attributes in successful poultry keeping.

Nevertheless, as science advances and the economics of production become more and more important, it is necessary to keep up to date and, if necessary, change methods to suit the times.

The purpose of this book is to give some insight into the principles and practice of rearing laying pullets. This, however, is merely an aid to, and not a substitute for, practical experience, gained under knowledgeable direction.

PENNY WISE— POUND FOOLISH

Cheapness and economy are not necessarily synonymous in poultry rearing, and deviating from sound feed or management practice to reduce costs may be bad economics.

The cost of rearing and maintaining a flock of pullets during their laying life must be met by revenue from eggs and the carcass value of the flock. Income from the flock's carcass value is steadily declining, particularly where smaller hybrids are being marketed in competition with low-priced broilers of almost similar size. Revenue from eggs is at least 90 per cent of the total income. In order to make this as high as possible, pullets must go into the laying house fit to stand a long laying period.

	s. d.	%	
REARING TO 16 WEEKS			
CHICK	3 6	28	
FEED	7 6	60	
LABOUR (Assuming £7 to £10 per week for 5,000 birds).	6	4	**19**% OF TOTAL COST
OTHER CHARGES	1 0	8	
	12 6	100%	
FROM 20 WEEKS TO SLAUGHTER (After 12 months of lay)			**81**% OF TOTAL COST
OVERALL COSTS	55 0		

Everything depends on a chick getting a good start in life.

A fair estimate of rearing costs is shown in the table opposite. It can be seen that cost of rearing is 19 per cent of the total cost from day-old to slaughter. Therefore a saving of 2s. 6d. on the cost of rearing is less than 5 per cent of the overall cost, and is offset by the income from 10 eggs.

Food Cost—Food costs are one and a half times all other costs. Although wastage must be avoided, it is false economy to judge quality on price or to economise on price per ton. In its first 20 weeks the average pullet eats about 24lb. of food, so that a difference of £5 a ton makes a difference of only 2d. a bird.

Chick Costs—What has been said regarding the quality and cost of feed is even more important in relation to chick costs. Mistakes in feeding can be quickly remedied, but the expected life of a chick is 18 months or more—a long time to use an inferior article. And the charges for feeding and housing are the same for good or bad chicks.

The choice of chick is generally made on the strength of expected performance in the laying house. The best selection is by following the results of Random Sample Testing, details of which incorporate rearing costs. Mortality rates are important—dead birds don't lay eggs, and a rearing mortality of 10 per cent means a charge of 1s. 6d. to each of the surviving birds. High mortality leads to further financial

7

loss because the laying house will be understocked and capital will not be fully exploited.

Other Charges—The item "Other Charges" includes depreciation on housing, feed for brooding, litter and any medications. If the charge for medications exceeds 1d. there is something wrong—either with the system, the selection of food or the chick. (This does not include vaccinating charges.)

Housing Costs—The cost of housing can be as low as 5s. a bird if old buildings are used for brooding and if there is plenty of cheap range housing. Modern intensive rearing houses cost about 12s. 6d. per square foot fully equipped, the cost per bird being greatly influenced by the amount of space given.

Again, be careful when cutting housing costs. Crowding or bad housing will result in reduced performance in the laying house. Cramming future layers at 1 square foot instead of 2 square feet when this is indicated may save a little on capital, but it puts a great strain on management.

Labour Costs—Success in rearing is dependent on the quality of management. With the older methods of rearing on grass, success depended on plenty of space, small unit size and attention to details. Modern intensive methods deal with larger units, and tend to economise on space and eliminate close attention. To compensate for these faults in intensive rearing, the management needs to be that much better.

There must be sound thinking by the person who plans the system and the person on the job. The labour cost for rearing a 16-week old pullet is about 6d. a bird; this assumes a wage of £7 to £10 a week for looking after 5,000 birds. This is equivalent to a rearing mortality of just over 3 per cent, or the income from 2 eggs a bird. Obviously, over-taxing the labour force to make "savings" involves great risks.

WHAT THE BIRD NEEDS

A lot of research work has been done to determine the requirements of poultry rearing and to develop practical systems to make them work. Except perhaps for the specialist poultry rearer, rearing is not an end in itself. The main object is a healthy, profitable layer.

Research work on rearing should be in the context of the bird's whole life. Much more information is needed on the effect and cost of all the factors contributing to a healthy, productive life.

As an illustration, there is now a trend towards expensive housing on litter or wire from day-old to 16 or 18 weeks. The system shows low mortality and produces birds that lay well; it has been adopted by many efficient, large producers and seems ideal for a rapid and large crop of first-year eggs.

Housing on wire or slats from day-old to 16 or 18 weeks produces birds that lay as well as those reared on range.

But is it fundamentally better than the system adopted by people who favour rearing the hard way?

In one extreme example of the latter, spring-hatched chicks are housed for 4 days and then left outside to fend for themselves. They progress in a makeshift way on grass with the minimum of food and little shelter. A few die, but the philosophy is that these are weaklings and are best dead. The rest grow on hard and tough, to become tardy but excellent layers.

Under this second system the birds cost little and they stand the pace. They could make good second-year layers if kept on. But it has not been established whether, and under what conditions, it is profitable to keep birds for two laying seasons.

Range rearing may be convenient on the general farm, but labour can be high, especially in bad weather.

Brooding Temperatures—Apart from a great deal being insufficiently well known, there is much conflicting research work on the environmental needs of the chick. Regarding optimium brooding temperatures for example, different recommendations are made by different research workers. Therefore the chick rearer must play for safety and stick to the following well-tried principles—he will not go very far wrong if he does, and remembers that no brooder can imitate the hen's knowing how far chicks can wander and just when they need her protective warmth.

(1) Brooder temperature for the day-old chick should be 95 degrees F.

(2) The brooder temperature may fall by 1 degree daily until it reaches atmospheric temperature.

(3) A room temperature of 70 degrees should be maintained at least for the first 14 days. This develops the chick's heat-control mechanism by encouraging movement outside the confines of the brooder.

(4) All draughts must be excluded until the birds are thoroughly conditioned to varying temperatures. Draughts are normally of the low, prevailing-outside temperature, and if birds are not conditioned to this they can develop chills, leading to unthriftiness or death.

Draughts must be excluded until the birds are well feathered. This is especially important with intensive rearing.

Ventilation—The problem of reconciling heat requirements with ventilation is also not fully understood. According to current practice, young chicks require a ventilation rate of 0·6 cubic feet per minute per lb. liveweight in winter, rising to 1·0 in summer. But too much ventilation is as bad as too little, especially in the early stages. To allow for birds of varying ages, and varying outside weather conditions, a wide range in ventilation rates is necessary. Controlled ventilation gives the best results.

Lighting—Lighting is beginning to be better understood. It is an important part of the chick's environment. Chicks will make reasonable growth with a wide variation in light treatments—from 24 hours of bright light normally daily, to 6 hours dim light daily. The latest work on broiler chicks, in fact, suggests they eat sufficient and make good growth in darkness!

These remarks refer only to the need for light as an aid to feeding, watering, getting about and so on. But light patterns also affect maturity and subsequent egg production. The actual pattern and its intensity depend on the hatch date and the pattern of laying desired—whether sexual maturity is to be reached at a natural time or whether it must be delayed for economic reasons. This subject is discussed fully on page 70.

Feeding—It goes without saying that a major requirement of rearing is meeting all the nutritional needs of the growing bird. A common failure is to neglect to follow up excellent chick rations with satisfactory rations for the subsequent

Feeders must be close to the brooders for young chicks; Keyes trays and chick-box lids may be used at first.

growing period. Again, this subject is dealt with fully on page 78.

It is no use providing the correct feed if the chicks are not able to make the best use of it. Enough feeders and drinkers must be within easy reach of the chicks in their early days. It may appear as though birds, drinkers and feeders, all placed near the heat, are too closely packed, but this does not matter. Birds must not range for nourishment until their heat-control is established, nor unless the room temperature is high enough not to strain their limited capacity to maintain heat.

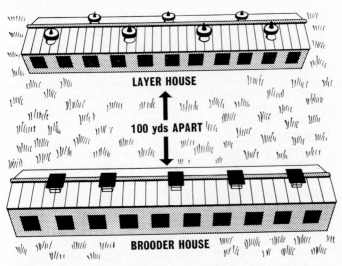

LAYER HOUSE

100 yds APART

BROODER HOUSE

Disease Prevention—Disease is a matter demanding constant attention. There is no point in providing the correct environment if it is allowed to become contaminated with disease. Therefore, a thorough cleaning of rearing equipment and a period of de-population are necessary before any new birds are introduced to the house. What *has* been extablished is that rearing houses should be placed well away from adult birds to avoid the risks of leucosis, and that full anti-coccidiosis precautions should be taken from day-old.

THE
BASIC
SYSTEMS

One rearing system cannot be said to be better than another if laying performance and mortality are similar, despite the current trend away from extensive systems towards highly-intensive systems. The reasons for this trend are the greater numbers of birds reared per unit, the lower labour costs, and the knowledge that intensively-kept birds are not inferior to range-reared birds, hitherto considered preferable. There is also the point that the large-scale investor wants to be certain of his returns; therefore all avoidable risks must be eliminated.

The rearing systems now in common use are single-stage intensive; multi-stage intensive; and multi-stage, followed by extensive.

Single-stage Intensive—This system of rearing may be done in three ways:

(1) On litter from day-old to date of entering the laying house (usually at 16 to 20 weeks).

(2) On wire or slats from day-old to point-of-lay. From day-old to 3 weeks it is usual to cover the floor with paper, hardboard, or polythene and shavings. There is also a trend towards taking birds through from day-old to end-of-lay in the same wire or slatted-floor house.

(3) In pullet-rearing batteries. Although this is not strictly single-stage, it can be classified this way because the birds do not leave the building in which they are raised. Basically, the batteries consist of a tier brooder to which extensions are added for each successive age. Birds move on through connecting openings, and there is a minimum of handling.

It is now common for pullets to be reared on broiler lines—that is on litter, as shown here.

Pullets reared throughout on wire do as well as those on litter. Shavings must be used for the first 3-4 weeks.

15

Pullet-rearing batteries are cheap, efficient and need little labour. (The cover on the scraper mechanism was removed for the photograph.)

The basic principles of broiler rearing apply also to single-stage pullet rearing. Apart from providing suitable heat, the most important factor in the early weeks is to exclude draughts. A fear of coccidiosis is the main reason for using wire instead of litter. In theory, brooder heat keeps the litter dry and restrains the development of coccidiosis. In practice, particularly in houses where ventilation is inefficient, it is difficult to keep the litter absolutely dry after the first few days of brooding—hence some preference for wire. Normal mesh wire is too large for young chicks, and until they are older an overlaying frame of small-mesh wire ($\frac{1}{2}$ in $\times$ $\frac{1}{2}$ in) is placed over the main wire frame under and around the brooder.

In connection with wire and litter floors, it is increasingly felt that fewer stresses will arise when birds are kept on the same kind of floor—indeed in the same general environment—throughout life.

There is much to be said for the pullet-rearing battery. If it is not overloaded, it is efficient, cheap and needs little labour. But general opinion is that in any rearing system the birds should be reared in one batch and the house de-populated between batches. The pullet-rearing battery does not follow these recommendations because it involves a constant throughput, which makes de-population difficult. Another problem is the provision of light patterns suitable for each age group.

Multi-stage Intensive—Most people start poultry rearing from small beginnings with miscellaneous items of multi-stage equipment. Once accustomed to the equipment and to the system, they are not likely to change to single-stage rearing, particularly these days when old equipment is almost unsaleable. In any case, many of them are general farmers with a number of spare buildings. In these circumstances a continuous throughput, with reasonable regard for disease control, is possible. All these advantages are too obvious to be discarded lightly.

*Tier brooders are satisfactory
for day-old to 3 or 4 weeks.
But makers generally
over-estimate the numbers held.*

Tier brooders have very localised heat, and can be placed in simple buildings that need not be fully insulated; birds in carry-on cages similarly housed do very well. The arguments for starting birds in tier brooders are strong—they get a good, warm, disease-free start and that is half the battle.

After this stage the problem is how to house them if they are not going outdoors. They can go into slatted or wire-floor growers' houses, converted open-fronted sheds, slatted lean-to's or similar accommodation. But there are difficulties with all of these. The environment is very different and settling-in can be a problem.

As already stated, it is best for a bird to keep to the same kind of housing or even the same house throughout life. On the whole, the most certain and trouble-free method is carry-on cages, which do not need elaborate housing. What is quite certain is that the risks of coccidiosis are so great that a transfer from wire to litter or grass is in-advisable. On the other hand, birds can go from grass or litter to wire or slats.

A new multi-stage development worth examining takes the birds in tier brooders to 7 weeks, then transfers them direct to laying cages Simple removable adaptations allow younger birds to eat comfortably In the early stages, each cage can accommodate a number of growers

The Californian Cage System—The Californian-cage layer system might well be adapted for carrying-on growers in this country. As used in America, birds are housed in long stretches of wire caging, sub-divided into sections each holding up to 20 birds. There are no walls, and a simple roof provides the only protection from the weather.

The advantages of the system are plenty of air (to combat respiratory diseases), easy removal of floor-dropped manure from the open sides, and cheap construction.

Although egg production drops in extreme heat or cold, this is a matter which would not apply if used for growers. The only disadvantage of housing them on this system could be a rise in food consumption in cold weather. But this would be no worse than some of the ways free-range birds are now managed.

The depressing conditions brought about by wind, rain and extreme cold could be alleviated by temporary and easily-removable sides. Straw bales, thatched frames, close-mesh

wire netting and similar barriers could be used. Water is
not likely to freeze if troughing and tanks are placed to make
use of rising body heat.

This system is not basically different from the static outdoor
systems now used successfully. But it is much cheaper, and
the buildings are easily constructed by farm labour.

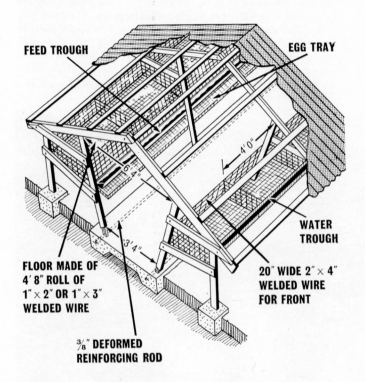

FEED TROUGH

EGG TRAY

4' 0"

**WATER
TROUGH**

**FLOOR MADE OF
4' 8" ROLL OF
1" × 2" OR 1" × 3"
WELDED WIRE**

3' 4"

**20" WIDE 2" × 4"
WELDED WIRE
FOR FRONT**

**⅜" DEFORMED
REINFORCING ROD**

Multi Indoor-Outdoor—There are numerous variations on
this system of rearing, including the following:

  (1) Tier brooders to hayboxes to range shelters.
  (2) Tier brooders to carry-on cages to range shelters.
  (3) Tier brooders to static hayboxes to static fold units.
  (4) Intensive litter to 8 weeks, followed by range
      shelters on grass.

19

In all these cases the danger of coccidiosis when going outdoors is very real. Expert use of coccidiostats is indicated, unless the ground is fresh and uncontaminated. But see page 94.

The difference between these systems and the multi-stage intensive is that the birds have access to unrestricted fresh air and sometimes to grass. However, it is doubtful if birds in hayboxes and folds get much more fresh air than those in controlled environment houses. Colds are not unknown in range shelters! The sole virtues in raising birds in such equipment are that they are kept in small units, and airborne disease is less likely to occur.

This range shelter is perhaps too simple. Walls should be solid to ground level, and roofing felt is hardly durable enough.

There can be no doubt about the value of good fresh grass, provided it is young and short. Otherwise crop troubles are bound to occur. But anyone who rears birds on grass must be a skilled feeder because *ad lib* consumption of grass, which varies greatly in quality, means that normal growth rate can be impaired.

Nevertheless, many farmers have successfully integrated pullet raising into general farming. Growing pullets may follow beef cattle around the farm to make the best use of the manure, as a supplement to fertilisers, and to provide plenty of grass at the right stage of growth for the cattle and poultry. But, apart from these factors, the value of outside rearing is difficult to substantiate. There may be unknown virtues in the system but they appear to have no great cash value—and that is the ultimate test.

Choice of Method—The choice of a rearing system depends on the ultimate aim of production. The many different types of enterprise in the egg industry indicate why there are so many systems and varieties of houses and equipment. One man, conscious of disease, will plump for single-stage rearing, preferably through to end-of-lay. Another may feel the same but be apprehensive about crushing, and will perhaps choose tier brooders and laying cages from 7 weeks onwards.

Looking at this situation objectively, it seems that a different approach is required. The answer is to base all calculations on a minimum egg price—say 2s. 4d. a dozen—and to plan rearing (and choice of chick, housing, equipment, etc.) so that price covers costs and leaves a margin for profit.

The heavy costs are labour, bird, house, and equipment depreciation. Labour is heavier for extensive systems and is likely to get progressively more expensive. Therefore, the future of outdoor systems is questionable—except with poultry on a general farm and where the farm is well integrated from the labour angle. Bird depreciation varies with the carcass value of culls (largely a matter of weight) and upon the rate of mortality experienced.

Over the years, the best health and accident-free records have been shown by off-the-floor rearing and laying. Least mortality occurs when stresses due to moving from one house to another are minimised. Least crushing occurs in cage rearing and cage laying—where bird units are small.

Lastly, feeding. Savings on outdoor feeding on grass are small and do not outweigh the possible disadvantages of outdoor rearing. As stated earlier, growers consume so little that a ration costing £5 per ton more than the average costs only 2d. more per bird to 16 weeks. The overall need is for minimum costs and maximum efficiency.

The final question is depreciation on equipment. If 10 per cent depreciation a year is taken as a standard, a comparison between systems can be made as follows:

	COST OF 5,000 BIRD THROUGHPUT ANNUALLY	DEPRECIATION PER BIRD
	£	s. d.
SINGLE STAGE LITTER	2,500	1 0
SINGLE STAGE WIRE	2,000	10
LITTER 0 to 8 WEEKS & RANGE SHELTERS	1,600	$7\frac{1}{2}$
TIER, HAYBOX, RANGE SHELTER	1,600	$7\frac{1}{2}$
REARING BATTERY	1,500	7

WHICH LAYING SYSTEM ?

There is not much difference between any of the intensive laying systems (in terms of net profit). Of course, housing, equipment and management must be good in every case, and the best birds must be chosen.

A hen-housed average of around 250 eggs a year is possible from batteries, wire floors, slatted floors or deep litter; however, batteries probably show the most consistent results. (See Table 1). And with lower prices and competition from Continental eggs, it is consistently high production that must be the aim.

How does rearing affect this situation? It affects it because high egg performance depends not only on the laying environment, but also on the birds being reared in such a way that they can develop their full potential egg production.

Important points such as chills in the early stages of rearing, disease prevention and good feeding have already been mentioned. Mortality is partly genetic in origin but mostly avoidable by good management. But some rearing systems may be better than others in this respect. However, the figures given in Table 1 show that it is possible (in a wide range of systems) to rear pullets capable of living a healthy, fully-productive life throughout the laying year. (The figures in the table are actual costs, all relating to a light-heavy cross.)

From the same table it appears that battery system No. 3 has obvious advantages. The system does consistently produce birds with a hen-housed average of 250 eggs, with a battery mortality of between 12 and 14 per cent. But one must be cautious about these figures, as the comments on page 26 show.

23

TABLE 1
Comparison of costs on intensive systems

COSTS	BATTERY 1		BATTERY 2		BATTERY 3	
	s.	d.	s.	d.	s.	d.
Food, grit	28	6	24	6	26	0
Light, power	1	6	1	6	1	6
Labour-routine	3	0	3	6	4	0
Labour, cleaning out and disinfecting	0	2	0	4	0	4
Depreciation	3	6	2	0	2	0
Interest	2	1	1	3	1	3
Return eggs h/h/a	240		250		250	
Mortality (%)	10		14		9	

TIER BROODER
REARING CAGES

0-8 WEEKS LITTER
8-16 WEEKS RANGE

FLOOR—HALF LITTER
HALF WIRE

System of rearing

4		WIRE FLOOR		SLATTED FLOOR NO FANS		DEEP LITTER	
s.	d.	s.	d.	s.	d.	s.	d.
26	3	25	6	29	0	29	0
1	6	1	6	0	4	1	6
1	6	2	0	2	6	2	0
0	4	0	3	1	3	0	4
1	9	2	0	1	9	3	0
1	1	1	3	1	1	1	9
240		240		235		240	
10		10		14		15	

**TIER BROODER
GROWING CAGES
STATIC SHELTERS**

**SINGLE STAGE SLATS
WITH LITTER 0-3 WEEKS**

**FLOOR LITTER,
THEN RANGE**

Referring to Table 2, (page 28), the variation in food consumption on rearing systems 1, 2, and 4, is not significant. It can be taken that feed costs for the three systems are likely to be the same, given the same strain of birds on rations of equal energy value. Occasionally, lower figures have been recorded, but they are probably due to deliberate or accidental feed restrictions.

System No. 3 with a long period of range feeding, does have lower feed costs. But greater accuracy in costing would probably show costs equal to those of the other systems. Grass cannot be grown for nothing and must bear its full share of farm overheads, as well as costs of labour, seeds and cultivation.

The figures for depreciation on housing and equipment cover new buildings and equipment, and also converted buildings. Again, system No. 3 appears to have low costs but it is doubtful if this is a true figure. Were tractor costs included? Men and machines are needed to move range shelters and to carry food. Again, it must be said that poultry accounts are often not complete on general farms. A proper share of general farm expenditure is probably not included in the table.

Then there is the question of volume of throughput, which affects the depreciation charge. This will be relatively low when de-population periods are short or non-existent. On the other hand, a restricted throughput to control disease raises the figure. Since airborne disease is less of a problem with outdoor systems and stringent de-population measures less necessary, one may expect in these days of increasing respiratory disease to see reduced depreciation charges from outdoor rearing. This indeed may cause a swing back to this practice.

But, overall, the most important factor in rearing costs is mortality. A mortality rate of 20 per cent (not uncommon a few years ago), can add 3s. to the cost of rearing each pullet. Where it is 3 per cent, the charge can be as low as 2d.

Summary—All systems of rearing can produce excellent layers. And, given good management, they all show similar costs for rearing. Unfortunately, good management cannot be guaranteed all the time by all producers. Therefore, other things being equal, the system of rearing most likely to reduce any errors of management is likely to be preferred.

Since disease, unthriftiness from mild attacks of disease, and accidents are most likely to increase rearing costs, affect laying performance and add to management stress, the likely system is one that can control disease and the conditions leading to disease.

It can be re-stated that no system beats another when management is of a high standard. Given this, however, the really important factor is choice of laying strain—not the rearing system.

FOR "£ROFITS" SAKE INSTALL CLEAN-EZIE LAYING BATTERIES

World Famous
Paper Cleaning
Battery

New patent electric glass base battery with all-chain drive awarded SILVER MEDAL Dairy Show 1962

New 2/3 Step
Battery

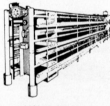

504 Bird Capacity
£230 10. 0.

1800 Bird Capacity
£847 0. 0.

1080 Bird Capacity
£453 15. 0.

JOHN SHEPHERD AND SONS LIMITED
CLIFTON ROAD BLACKPOOL   PHONE · BLACKPOOL 61212 (5 lines)

TABLE 2
Comparison of charges on intensive systems

SYSTEM	FOOD		DEPRECIATI○ OF HOUSE EQUIPMEN⟨	
	s.	d.	s.	d.
TIER BROODER & REARING CAGES	6	6	1	0
FLOOR LITTER (NEW HOUSE)	6	0	1	2
0-8 WEEKS LITTER 8-18 WEEKS RANGE	5	8	0	4
0-3 WEEKS TIER BROODER CARRY-ON CAGES 3-8 WEEKS STATIC SHELTER 8-16 WEEKS	6	6	0	9

ABOUR	LIGHT & HEAT	INTEREST	MORTALITY CHARGE	TOTAL
s. d.	s. d.	s. d.	s. d.	s. d.
0 6	0 3	0 4	0 2	9 0
0 3	0 3	0 8	0 1	8 5
0	0 2	0 2	0 3	7 7
0	0 2	0 6	0 2	9 1

HOUSING AND EQUIPMENT

The main requirements of a chick in the early days of life are constant warmth, and a place to find food and water.

All brooders provide this, and the sole function of a house is to provide protection from draughts and external temperatures that would affect the brooder temperature, which should remain near the right level unless altered by the poultryman. Quite simple buildings are able to do all that is needed in this respect. An experienced man needs surprisingly simple housing and equipment when the numbers being reared are small. But it may be neither safer nor economic with large flocks.

However, there is much to be said for the other view—that good housing always pays. Whatever the brooder used, room temperatures should be 70 deg. at the start. This is more cheaply and readily provided by a well-built and insulated house (with the minimum of additional space heating), than an uninsulated house where the temperature may be too high in summer and too low in winter. Considerable expenditure is necessary to keep uninsulated houses at the right temperature during cold spells and, even then, it is difficult to maintain the right conditions. When that happens mortality increases—and mortality is the biggest factor in the cost of rearing replacement pullets.

Copy Broiler Methods—Broiler growers would be unable to stay in business if they accepted the mortality rates experienced by many pullet rearers using simple equipment. Therefore, there is much to be learned from their methods. Almost without exception, they rear on the floor in houses that are well insulated (both roof and walls), have no windows (windows are incompatible with efficient wall insulation, and often with vice control), and with controlled ventilation. Consequently, in winter when outside temperatures are low, temperatures inside the house are up to what is required for young chicks still in the brooding stage (heat from the brooders is the only space heating normally required), and correct when they are off heat.

*This house is well insulated, but the ventilation may be difficult.
The fan and the wall inlets suggest conflicting air currents.*

The temperatures in a broiler house are also correct for optimum food conversion. Apart from the factor of mortality, broilers can only pay if meat is produced at the least cost in food, which is the most expensive item in chick raising whether for broilers or egg strains. Inefficient housing means inefficient food conversion.

For anyone who raises a large number of pullets each year, there is little doubt that chicks should be started in a good brooder placed in a house in which the required temperatures can be easily and simply maintained. And remember that insulation materials are cheaper than artificial heat. (All this effort to make the best use of food is wasted if inefficient feeders, wasting a great deal of food, are used!)

Insulation—Good insulation of the surfaces of a building maintains warmth in winter and prevents overheating in summer. Also, properly-applied insulation can stop condensation and keep the building dry. At the same time the warm, inside surfaces help the natural air flow.

31

"U" values of roof and wall constructions

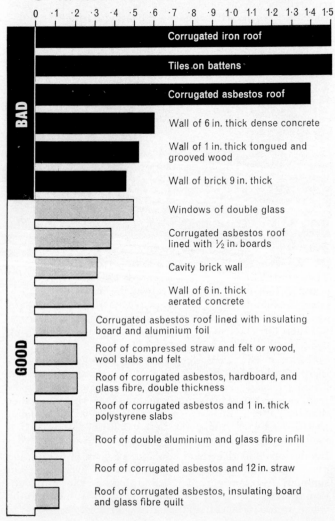

0 ·1 ·2 ·3 ·4 ·5 ·6 ·7 ·8 ·9 1·0 1·1 1·2 1·3 1·4 1·5

BAD

Corrugated iron roof

Tiles on battens

Corrugated asbestos roof

Wall of 6 in. thick dense concrete

Wall of 1 in. thick tongued and grooved wood

Wall of brick 9 in. thick

GOOD

Windows of double glass

Corrugated asbestos roof lined with ½ in. boards

Cavity brick wall

Wall of 6 in. thick aerated concrete

Corrugated asbestos roof lined with insulating board and aluminium foil

Roof of compressed straw and felt or wood, wool slabs and felt

Roof of corrugated asbestos, hardboard, and glass fibre, double thickness

Roof of corrugated asbestos and 1 in. thick polystyrene slabs

Roof of double aluminium and glass fibre infill

Roof of corrugated asbestos and 12 in. straw

Roof of corrugated asbestos, insulating board and glass fibre quilt

Insulation can be achieved by "dead" air spaces; by using materials of low thermal conductivity; and heat reflective materials.

The effectiveness of insulating materials can be measured by their "U" and "K" values. The "U" value (or thermal transmittance value) is the amount of heat that passes hourly through a certain form of construction 1 square foot in area, when there is a difference of 1 degree F. between the temperatures on either side. The "K" value is the heat loss through 1 square foot of material, 1 inch thick, per 1 degree F. difference in temperature between the two surfaces The tables here show the insulating values of various materials and forms of construction.

"K" values of insulating materials

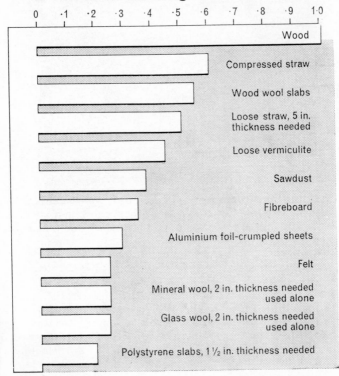

| | 0 | ·1 | ·2 | ·3 | ·4 | ·5 | ·6 | ·7 | ·8 | ·9 | 1·0 |

Wood

Compressed straw

Wood wool slabs

Loose straw, 5 in. thickness needed

Loose vermiculite

Sawdust

Fibreboard

Aluminium foil-crumpled sheets

Felt

Mineral wool, 2 in. thickness needed used alone

Glass wool, 2 in. thickness needed used alone

Polystyrene slabs, 1½ in. thickness needed

It is suggested that for lightly-insulated houses, a "U" value of 0·3 or less is satisfactory. For intensive housing, particularly where artificial heat is used, a standard of from 0·2 to 0·1 is necessary.

In most buildings the roof deserves the most attention, and presents most difficulties. The greatest problems are concerned with suspending insulating materials cheaply, and in establishing a vapour seal (See opposite) The walls and floors should not be neglected, and where there is a concrete floor it should incorporate a damp-proof course and insulation.

A damp course is a 'must' in all dwarf walls; roofing felt is satisfactory.

Building Construction—Walls must be weather proof, provide the required insulation, be easily cleaned, and able to withstand high-pressure water on the inside. Walls based on timber are generally best clad with $\frac{3}{4}$-inch cedar, with asbestos partition board for the inside. There should be a brick, block or concrete dwarf wall, with a damp course.

Where the wall or roof construction does not provide sufficient insulation, the material added must resist damage by vermin, have the required "U" value, and be durable and cheap. It may also provide a lining and vapour barrier. A reflective aluminium foil facing the inside can be effective. Loose, "in-fill" insulation is not generally suitable for walls.

The roof must be waterproof, stressed to take snow and wind loads, and should need the minium of maintenance. Aluminimum is at present only suitable when the air is clean and the site is away from the sea; asbestos cement is likely to be the cheapest roofing.

The whole construction should be smooth and free of projections, such as rafters, inside. Any partitions and fittings should be removable.

Vapour Seals—Unless the rising, warm, damp air is barred from finding its way into the insulating material and from thence to the cold outer skin, the efficiency of the insulation will be greatly reduced and in time the materials will be ruined. Warm, moisture-laden air in contact with cold surfaces precipitates condensation which, in the absence of insulation, drips to the ground causing damp litter. Where there is insulation the damp air causes a gradual soddening and therefore deterioration. **The function of a vapour seal is to prevent these troubles.**

The vapour barrier must be sealed so that no damp air reaches the insulation.

Any impervious and waterproof material is suitable as a vapour seal, provided all the joints are well sealed. Those less-waterproof may be painted with two coats of aluminium paint.

The many simple and successful forms of insulation used in old farm buildings (successful in the sense that the buildings are kept reasonably warm and cool as the season may be, and are free from condensation) are usually due to high roofs, and the large air spaces between them and the false ceilings installed. Air movement is brisk enough to prevent condensation, especially if there are air gaps at the eaves. Such conversions are not efficient according to the book, but they seem to work well in many cases.

The fact is that the fundamental data for designing efficient houses are still inadequate and, where they do seem adequate, it is often difficult to ensure that a sound design works when the house is actually erected. Even standard designs often seem to develop faults when they are put into use.

A great deal depends on the actual site used. Large areas of concrete surrounding a house can raise the external temperature on hot days. Conversely, a house surrounded by trees keeps cool, although it may be damp in winter.

Floors—Whether the ventilation and insulation of a house are efficient—and their effects are closely correlated—is shown in deep-litter houses by the litter. When the house is working efficiently, the litter is friable or crumbly (always assuming that the stocking rate is right).

Given good ventilation and insulation, bacterial action can deal with a given amount of droppings—and no more. Depending on the size of the house, the bird and the flock, the right density for an all-litter house varies between 4 and 2 sq. ft. per bird. The larger the house and the more birds there are, the less room per bird is required, and conversely. More space is needed if the soil is not free-draining, which is the ideal. Clay soils are best improved by being covered with a layer of chalk or sand before the litter is spread, but here a concrete floor is perhaps best in the long run. It must have a damp-proof course but, even so, may not be thoroughly dry and satisfactory until it has been in use for a year. An insulant is also necessary; for instance air bricks or, more cheaply, a fibreglass quilt laid under the top screed.

Stocking density also depends on whether the floor is wholly litter, or part litter and part slats or wire. In these circumstances, where birds spend the night on the raised platform and where they also spend a great deal of time feeding and

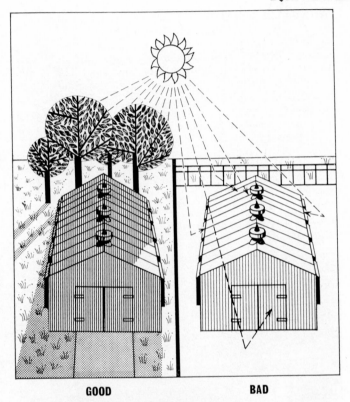

GOOD   **BAD**

drinking, a high proportion of the droppings and all the water spillage pass into the non-litter area. This greatly reduces the working load on the litter and allows greater density.

For birds up to 16 weeks old on all litters, from 0·85 to 2·0 sq. ft. a head should be allowed according to age.

Droppings Pits—The droppings pit should have an area of at least ½ square foot a bird, and should be placed in the centre of the house for best ventilation and ease of cleaning out. The sides should be 24 to 30 inches high, removable, and of preserved wood. Sections of mesh or netting, and 2 in × 2 in. perches, at 15 to 18 in. centres should be placed on top.

37

Wire and Slatted Floors—A 3-foot clearance under the floor is standard, but could be 2 feet for growers. In timber buildings, dwarf walls must not be less than 3 feet above ground level. A concrete floor beneath slats or wire is necessary on all but light, well-drained soils. The ground floor inside must not be below the outside ground level.

Wire floors of 3 in. × 1 in. mesh are standard, and for older growers 3 in. × ½ in. is probably best as a general compromise. The mesh should be 10 or 12 gauge, not galvanised, in sections up to 7½ ft. × 4 ft. The edges can be framed with 3 in. × 1½ in. timber. The timbers of adjacent sections can be supported at the corners and half-way along the long sides by solid pillars (these can be hollow concrete blocks, oil drums, or concrete-filled drain pipes). There should be 2 in. × 2 in. perches on the floor, at 15 to 18 in. centres.

Clearance under the floors depends on the birds—2 feet is enough for growers; 3½ feet for layers.

Slatted floors can be in sections up to 6 feet square, using slats ¾ to 1¼ in. deep, spaced 1¼ in. apart. The ends of the slats should rest on timbers supported on pillars. The timbers can be 4 in. × 2 in., supported at 4 ft. centres.

Tractor cleaning-out is economical, but it needs wide doors and well-spaced pillars.

The width of a house in relation to the total area is very important—the wider the house the better is the ventilation and therefore the condition of the litter. Ideally, for large units, 30 ft. to 40 ft. should be aimed at. On the other hand small houses, up to 25 ft. wide, with a droppings pit, reasonably steep-pitched roof and natural ventilation can be satisfactory. However, inlets and outlets must be adjustable, with the inlet area 3 times that of the outlet area.

To ease cleaning out, it is important to have wide (but draught proof) doors. Doors 10 feet wide at each end of the house will give access to a tractor and fore-end loader. A clear span without internal posts is therefore an advantage. Costs of the various houses and floors used for growers stocks depend on the type, and whether they are bought as commercial houses or built with farm labour. All-wire or slatted houses taking one bird per square foot cost about £1 a bird for house, floor and all the necessary equipment. An all-litter house with less-dense stocking will probably cost 25s. od. a bird. (See page 52 for a discussion of housing costs.)

39

A HOUSE ON TRIAL

At Stoke Mandeville, Bucks, the British Oil and Cake Meal Ltd. experimental house described below is giving excellent results from broiler trials, and it may set the pattern for the future in this type of housing. The house measures 150 ft. × 40 ft., and houses 4,000 birds in units of 250. The pens are separated by 3 ft. solid walls and observations suggest that this feature has a marked effect on holding down fowl paralysis.

The Walls—The walls and ends of the building consist of an outer leaf of brick and an inner leaf of 3 in. hollow clay tiles. The 2 in. cavity between them is filled with resin-bonded fibre glass. This construction was adopted after research had shown that the normal "U" value of 0·28 for an 11 in. cavity wall could be halved by filling the cavity with fibre glass, and that this would provide double the insulation value.

Three rows of air bricks run the full length of the walls, about 5 ft. from the floor, to provide an outlet for foul air.

The Roof—The roof has a pitch of only 4 degrees, and consists of an asbestos overlapping sandwich, supported on steel trusses. This also contains an interfill of 2 inches of fibre glass, with a polythene vapour seal, providing a "U" value of 0·14

The Floor—The floor consists of four layers. First a 4 in. layer of ashes; 3 in. of concrete on top of that; then a 3 in. layer of hollow clay tiles (set on a covering of pitch); and finally 1½ in. of concrete laid on top of the tiles. This construction also provides a "U" value of 0·14. Roof, walls and floors are therefore all insulated to the same degree. (The floor is possibly better insulated than it need be.)

Room Temperature—Thermometers are placed throughout the house and outside the building. When outside temperatures are at freezing point, the insulation system maintains a 30 to 40 degrees F. rise; in summer temperatures of 80 to 90 degrees F. the house remains at about 70 degrees F.

Ventilation and Humidity—The ventilation system is contrary to conventional British practice. To enable even distribution of air into each 16 ft. × 16 ft. pen, air is drawn into the far end of the house by four "L"-type 19 in. axial fans, running at 2,900 rpm. These drive the air into four 16 in. calico bags extending the full length of the building,

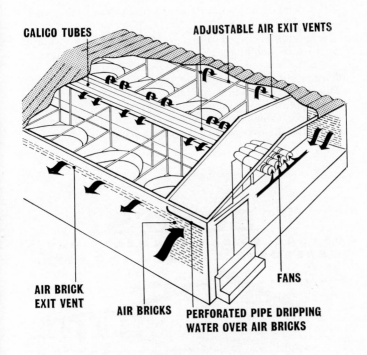

CALICO TUBES   ADJUSTABLE AIR EXIT VENTS

AIR BRICK
EXIT VENT

AIR BRICKS   PERFORATED PIPE DRIPPING
WATER OVER AIR BRICKS

FANS

giving a surface area of 460 square feet each. Thence it is
diffused under slight pressure into the pens, and out via the
air bricks. A simple, adjustable baffle guards the exit into
the air bricks.

At the far end of the house (where the air is drawn in), the
end walls and the side walls form part of a chamber. The
sides consist almost entirely of air bricks, which can be
saturated with water by means of perforated hose-piping
running along the outside of the building. In this way, in-
coming air can be moistened. In warm, sunny weather the
relative humidity in the pens was as low as 40 per cent, and
since this might have predisposed the birds to respiratory

41

infections, the air was moistened to prevent this occurring. The procedure also cools the air by more than 10 degrees F. in hot weather.

The fans are arranged so that 1 cubic foot of air is available per 1 lb. liveweight per minute at all times. For this purpose, one of the fans operates at half strength when necessary, and delivers only 2,100 instead of 4,500 cubic feet per minute. This ventilation rate is maintained from day-old until the chicks are three-weeks old, when they weigh approximately $\frac{1}{2}$ lb. each. Obviously this system demands a stand-by generator to take over when power cuts occur.

BOYD'S

CONTROLLED ENVIRONMENT HOUSING.
BREEDERS, LAYERS & BROILERS.

For rearing on Deep Litter, Slats or Weldmesh.

★ Clear Span Buildings from 18'—48' at no extra cost.
★ Cladded with 1" thick clear Western Red Cedarwood.
★ Controlled Ventilation by Automatic System.
★ Thermal insulation (U=.10.)
★ Windowless.

D. BOYD & SON LTD. McMULLEN ROAD, DARLINGTON
Co. DURHAM   Tel : 5864

EQUIPMENT

In Britain there is a need for an organised system of equipment testing, because a great deal of what is sold appears on the market before its defects have been revealed during hard, commercial use. Some examples of deficiencies are spillage and fouling of waterers, with sluggish and easily-blocked valves; wastage in feeders (particularly with mash); and the short life of tier brooders and similar equipment caused by poor galvanising.

For these reasons great care has to be exercised in choosing equipment. Fortunately, there is a wide selection of equipment to choose from. The main reasons why there is such a variety of equipment are differences in the size of flocks reared and in the systems of management employed. These, in turn, depend much on whether the poultry enterprise is being fitted into an existing economic unit, such as a general farm, or whether it is a new specialist unit. In the following pages the major items of poultry-rearing equipment are discussed and costed.

BROODER EQUIPMENT

Infra-red lamps—Used at the rate of one 250-watt red or white bulb to every 60 day-old chicks, these popular and useful heaters are suitable when small numbers are reared. Unless the surround is high and close enough to the lamps, chills from down-draughts can be expected. The bulbs produce localised heat, which leaves an otherwise unheated room cold—and if they cease to function, there is no reserve of heat.

Dull emitters—These bulbs have a longer and more certain life; if placed under a canopy, they preserve a little heat should the current go off.

Suspended Hovers—Using oil, gas or electricity, these are used for rearing from 50 to 1,000 day-olds, depending on the diameter of the hover and heat output. Brooders of this type are admirable because the heat is reflected on to the birds' back, while keeping the floor warm and dry. But a surround is essential. Less heat is required if the canopy is insulated. A thermostat is essential with all but the smallest sizes.
Price varies from £3 to £40.

43

Infra-red bulbs are cheap, and weaning is made easy by removing a bulb occasionally.

With suspended hovers, heat can be reduced by fuel adjustments and by raising the canopy. Cleaning-out is eased by raising the hover.

Wooster brooder—A variation of the above. It has a 4 ft.-square box top, which is filled with shavings. Beneath the box, which is supported on adjustable legs, are two 250-watt heaters—one infra-red and one dull emitter. This brooder must be used in an insulated, heated room, kept at 70 degrees F. during early brooding. It takes 250-300 chicks. **Price** £8. 10. 0d.

Tier brooders—Wire-floored tier brooders with a central heating pad are very satisfactory for chicks up to the age of 3 weeks. Chicks are confined so that they cannot stray from heat, food or water. There is no danger of coccidiosis. Labour is minimised. Tier brooders are often made three or four tiers high. At 3 weeks the chicks must be moved on to cooler cages in a warm room or there may be some over-crowding, with the consequent risk of vices starting.

44   **Price** £100 for 500 chicks, to £330 for 1,600 chicks.

Carry-on cages—These are of two main types—(1) taking birds from 3 to 8 weeks (the manufacturers often say 4 to 8 weeks, but see last item); and (2) from 3 weeks by stages, i.e., different sized cages to point-of-lay.

On large units, birds reared through on wire prove just as good layers as those reared outside. And labour is at a minimum. Depreciation—spread over a large number of birds—is reasonable. The only difficulty is arranging for proper de-population measures and, in some cases, dismantling and cleaning of the equipment.

Price   (i) 200 birds (without scraper cleaning equipment)
£55

(ii) 500 birds to point-of-lay (with scraper cleaning and automatic watering)—£350

Rearing in cages is easy, relatively cheap, and mortality is nearly always very low.

Cages for older birds must be robust, and easily dismantled for cleaning.

45

Haybox brooders—For those who insist on rearing birds out of doors as soon as they can be weaned from heat, and who like small units, the haybox brooder is useful. They take—at most—40 birds at 3 weeks, decreasing to about 25 birds at 8 weeks. The brooders need to be shifted every day unless used on static wire platforms, when labour-saving automatic waterers can be used. Unless disturbed by foxes, birds reared in these brooders grow on well with negligible mortality.

Price about £10.

Range shelters—These are used to take birds on from haybox brooders or from intensive houses, where in both cases the birds are taken to 8 weeks. Usually 10 ft. × 9 ft., range shelters hold 100 to 125 birds. They have wire—sometimes slatted—floors and, to be fully useful, should contain a feed hopper for use in bad weather and when the birds are shut up for a couple of days on being shifted to them. They should be on skids to enable them to be frequently shifted as an anti-worm and coccidiosis measure. Shutting-up is a nuisance in fox country.

Price —£40 to £50—(less if farm made).

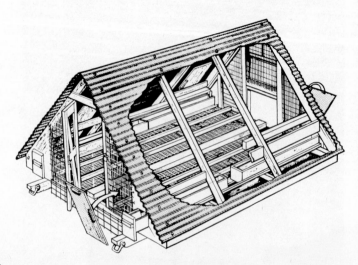

FEEDERS

It is said that the average cost of food wasted by a layer is at least 3s. od. a year. Assuming 100 lb. of feed consumed by a layer and 25 lb. during rearing, we may assume 9d. a bird as the figure for wastage by growers. This can be largely avoided by choice of suitable feeders. So too can fouling, due to lack of spinners or bad spinner design.

Chick feeders—As soon as a chick has become accustomed to feeding well from Keyes trays or chick-box tops (say after 4 days), it can graduate to a flat floor trough. This must be fitted with a spinner if waste is to be avoided. One problem is to keep shavings out of the feed. This difficulty must remain until they are able to perch while feeding from troughs raised off the floor, or big enough to feed from tube feeders suspended at the right height. It is partly to overcome these difficulties that battery brooders and wire-floor intensive houses have become more popular. However, this point should not be laboured because wastage is not great considering the small amount chicks eat.

Price   flat feeders: 18 in. long 8s. 6d.
            36 in. long 13s.

A stout, ready-adjustable spinner is essential on chick feeders, and birds must not be able to get into the trough.

Tube feeders are popular for large intensive houses, whether litter or wire. Holding from 15 to 30 lb. of food they cost from 20s. to 30s. They are very wasteful of mash even when carefully set, but they vary greatly in the amount of crumbs they waste; most are waste-proof with the pellets used for older birds. Their great advantage is that being suspended they leave the floor clear and, in effect, give more room per bird.

From 8 weeks old, floor-reared birds are most economically raised using "V"-shaped troughs placed on stands. Work at the National Institute of Poultry Husbandry has recently produced suitable designs for home manufacture of these feeders, although no doubt these designs will soon be faithfully and economically produced by commercial firms.

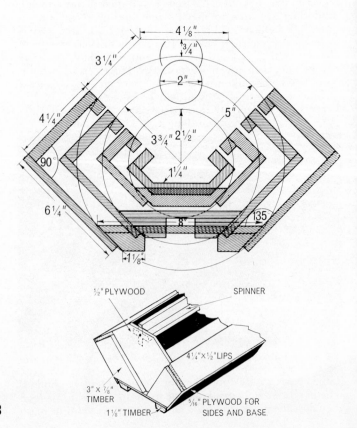

*Design of tube feeders is diff-
icult. Those with straight sides
are apt to 'bridge'; best feeds
are crumbs and pellets.*

*Birds take readily to auto-
matic feeders and, when the
meal level is set low, no waste
is possible.*

Automatic feeders—Set at their lowest level, automatic
feeders can be used for birds 2 weeks old and above. They
are the most waste-proof of all feeders and seem to stimulate
appetites. Four or five important manufacturers produce
them, and all now seem to have got over their teething
troubles. It is best to have a cleaner fitted to filter out the
shavings, which are inevitable on litter when the trough is
set low. Two inches per bird is reckoned adequate feeding
space for growers. Large rearers will consider that automatic feeding is economic for flocks of 2,000 taken to 16
weeks.

Price—For layers the cost is 5s. per bird for a flock of 500,
3s. for 2,000, and 2s. for 3,000.

49

FEEDING SPACE & WATER REQUIREMENTS

	FEED SPACE REQUIRED		DAILY WATER CONSUMPTION per 100 birds
	DRY MASH	CONTROLLED FEEDING	
8 TO 12 WEEKS	$2\frac{1}{2}$ ins	$3-3\frac{1}{2}$ ins	3 galls
12 TO 16 WEEKS	$3-3\frac{1}{2}$ ins	$3\frac{1}{2}-4$ ins	4 galls
18 TO 24 WEEKS	4 ins	5-6 ins	6 galls

DRINKERS

Drinkers should remain clean, prevent fouling, be easily cleaned, and prevent flicking (which causes damp litter). If they are automatic, they should have valves that are trouble-free or easily removed for cleaning, and which allow a rapid refill when the demand is high—birds tend to drink more at some times than others. It is important that birds should not have far to walk to get water; therefore, a large number of small water points is better than a few large ones. This is especially true when mash is fed, because it needs washing down with frequent sips of water.

Weight-operated Fox valve type—Opinions differ about these drinkers—some rearers have trouble with sticking valves and some do not. Some find that these 4 to 6 ft.-long drinkers take up a lot of room, others do not seem to mind. Nevertheless, there is a tendency to cut down the number to a minimum. On the whole they are reliable; spare parts are easily fitted and they are easily cleaned. One per 100 growers should be placed in the house.

Price £5 to £7.

Automatic bowl type—These mostly originated in Scandinavia where they are still favoured. Some fill quickly, others are sluggish, but this is a point that is more important

for layers than growers. Some have finicky, even Schrader-type valves, others have simple, stronger parts. Get a report from someone who has used them satisfactorily over a long period.
Price £2 to £3 10s. od.

The valves on Fox-valve drinkers should be cleaned frequently to avoid trouble.

A 'parrot-cage' drinker prevents 'flicking' and damp litter.

Continuous trickle drinkers are not as popular as they should be. The water is clean, but a header tank is essential.

51

Continuous trickle drinkers—Normally these are home-made. Angle iron or other suitable troughing is supported at the correct (and adjustable height), either down the middle of the house or along the walls. Usually a trickle of water from a controlling tap flows along to exit through a waste pipe taken to an outside drain. There is inevitable waste of water but, on the other hand, the supply is always clean and cool. The trough is kept at the right height by a small "dam" at the end of the drinker next to the overflow waste pipe. Trouble can arise at night when mains pressure rises; the flow can also be too slow during the day if a header tank is allowed to get low. The remedy is a ball valve on the mains supply to keep the header tank topped up.

Price —These simple installations are extremely cheap.

REARING HOUSES

Single-stage controlled environment.

> 1,000 Bird Unit—Controlled-environment house 30 ft. × 40 ft., of red cedar wood. Litter floor with central. slatted floor. Monorail and food carrier. 18-in. fans, cowls, all electrical gear, tube feeders and automatic drinkers. Infra-red brooders. Food store.
> **Price** complete, erected on prepared foundations and dwarf walls £1,065.

> 5,000 Bird Unit—Controlled-environment house 130 ft. × 48 ft. with all equipment.
> **Price** £3,690

> 1,000 Bird Unit—Weldmesh floor, controlled environment for birds to 16 weeks. 60 ft. × 30 ft. Fully insulated. Complete with 40 tube feeders, 4 auto drinkers, chick founts and infra-red lamps, fans, speed regulators and thermostat.
> **Price** £1,409

> 2,540 Bird Unit—House 30 ft. × 168¼ ft., with weldmesh floor. All ventilation, but no feeding or watering equipment.
> **Price** erected £3,019

Broiler house (could be used for pullet rearing):—

5,000 Bird Unit—120 ft. × 40 ft. red cedar wood house, with full ventilation, feeders, drinkers, gas brooders, monorail bulk feeder. **Price** erected £2,400.

Note: At 2 sq. ft. per bird on litter, this house would hold approximately 2,500 birds and need less equipment. With a wire floor at 3s. 9d. extra per sq. ft., it would hold (with full equipment) 5,000 birds at a total cost of 13s. 4d. per bird.

Two-stage cage rearing in controlled-environment house:—

1,000 Bird Unit:	£	s.	d.
House 36 ft. × 18 ft.	370	5	0
Partition	22	14	0
Erection	34	16	0
Fans, regulators, thermostat	88	5	6
Cages: Brooders 0-4 weeks	212	0	0
carry-on 4-16 weeks	567	15	0
	£1,295	15	6

Note: Foundations and floor to be provided by buyer.

Houses with natural ventilation:—

16 ft. × 19 ft. Windows, roof, end and sides lined	235	0	0
40 ft. × 19 ft. Windows, roof, end and sides lined	450	0	0
25 ft. × 24½ ft. Windows, lined with cedar wood	286	0	0
25 ft. × 80½ ft. Windows, lined with cedar wood	800	0	0
32 ft. × 19 ft. Wood wall ends, asbestos roof, no lining	147	0	0
16 ft. × 10 ft. Wood wall ends, asbestos roof, no lining	67	10	0

Note: Prices do not include erection.

53

Outside rearing units:—
             £ s. d.
  Haybox brooders—40 chicks
  from 3 or 4 weeks to 8 weeks.
  9½ ft. long   12 0 0
  9 ft. long   11 11 0
  (with wire floor for run)   14 0 0

Range shelters:—
  For 120 to 150 birds (maker's
  figures) weldmesh floor, wood
  panel back, open wire front
  with door, roof coming well
  down, fox-proof.   39 15 0

BROODERS

Tier brooders:—
  Types available include:
  500 chicks from 0 to 4 weeks—
  5 tiers, heated by bottled gas
  or electric, length 5 ft. 6 in.,
  width 4 ft. 2 in., height 5 ft.
  7 in.   106 0 0

  600 heavies from 0 to 4 weeks—
  4 tiers heated by bottled gas or
  electric, thermostat to each
  tier. Average consumption for
  4 tiers: 1½ to 2 cu. ft. bottled
  gas an hour, mains gas 8 to 10
  cu. ft. an hour, electricity 1¼
  to 1½ watts an hour. Floor area
  8 ft. × 3 ft.   145 0 0

  600 chicks from 0 to 4 weeks—
  4 tiers, heated by bottled gas or
  electric (£12 extra), length 8 ft.,
  width 4ft. 4 in., height 6 ft.
  4 in.   97 0 0

  1,600 hybrids from 0 to 4 weeks
  —4 tiers, with nursery runs,
  scraper cleaning plus dropping
  pans, auto watering, heated by
  gas or electric, length 21 ft. ×
  2 ft. 9 in. wide.   331 0 0

	£	s.	d.

500 chicks from 0 to 6 weeks—4 tiers, heated by gas or electric, length 11 ft., width 4 ft., height 6 ft. 2 in., paper cleaning. 148 0 0

Follow-on cages:—

Types available include:
500 birds from 4 weeks to point-of-lay—with scraper cleaning, auto-watering. 350 0 0

200 birds from 4 to 8 weeks—4 tiers, 5ft. 3 in. long, 6 ft. 4 in. high, 4 ft. 4 in. wide. 55 0 0

Electric scraper cleaning to serve number of stages, additional cost 102 0 0

Two-stage (paper cleaning):
500 birds from 6 to 12 weeks—3 tiers, 26 ft. × 6 ft. × 4 ft. 213 0 0
500 birds from 12 to 18 weeks—3 tiers, 41 ft. × 6 ft. × 4 ft. 322 0 0

Brooders, various:—

Infra-red lamps (with reflector) clear or red bright emitter lamp, for 60 to 75 chicks. 2 0 0

Dull emitter elements, in reflector, 500 watts, for 200 chicks 6 0 0

Dull emitter plate elements with 3 ft. canopy, 600 watts, for 200 chicks 7 0 0

Broiler type, bottle gas, canopy brooders for 1,000 chicks. Price depending mostly on insulation and finish 24 0 0 to 45 0 0

"Radisil" infra-red heaters, using element with silica tube and wire spiral, 725 watts, 200 to 250 chicks 3 17 0 to 4 5 0

55

Foster mother or Wooster type
(heated by 2 infra-red lamps),
for 200 chicks   8   0   0

Chick feeders with spinners:—

	£	s.	d.
12 in.		7	0
18 in.		8	6
24 in.		10	0
36 in.		13	0

Tubular feeders:—

	£	s.	d.
Capacity 20 lb.	1	1	0
„ 30 lb.	1	8	0
„ 40 lb.	1	9	0
„ 50 lb.	2	7	0

Deep-litter type floor troughs:
6 ft. long without legs, holding   up to
½ cwt., 25 to 30-bird size from   1   5   0
6 ft. long with legs, holding ½
cwt.   4   10   0

Monorail bulk feeders:—

Steel feed carrier 6 ft. × 2 ft. ×
2 ft.   19   0   0
Wheeled bearing trolley   3   5   0
Tubular track, per ft.   4   6

Automatic feeding:—

Quoted for 5,000 sq. ft. wire-
floor house, taking 5,000 birds
to 16 weeks   420   0   0
1 gallon chick founts   17   9

Drinkers:—

Broiler type, tank and ball-
cock, 7 ft. long, 150-bird size   5   5   0

Weight-operated   fox-valve
type, 6 ft. long, hanging   4   13   0

Weight-operated   fox-valve
type, 8 ft. long, on stand, 200
bird size   6   16   0

Scandinavian bowl type for 100
birds, Schrader valve control   2   9   0

FLOORS

Wire and slatted:—

£ s. d.

Manufacturers' quotation for wire and slatted floors, conveyed and fitted to customers' house (per square foot);

1¼ in. slats, 1⅜ in. apart, on 7 ft. × 3 ft. frames   2   6

3 in. × 1 in. 12 gauge weldmesh on 1¼ in. slats, 1⅜ in. apart, on 7 ft. × 3 ft. frames   3   9

Note: The above are suitable for growers from 8 weeks to point-of-lay.

½ in. woven-mesh brooder floors for fitting in brooders or for super-imposing on slats or weldmesh at day old   3   6

Supported floor panels:—

Slatted, American type, 1½ in. to 2 in. slats placed upright, showing ½ in. width, spaced 1 in. apart, 10 ft. × 4 ft. frames   4 15 0

3 in. × 1 in. weldmesh 12 gauge, 10 ft. × 4 ft. frames   4 15 0

3 in. × ½ in. weldmesh, 12 gauge, 10 ft. × 4 ft. frames   5 15 0

GENERAL POINTS ON MANAGEMENT

It is evident from earlier discussions on the merits of the various rearing systems that what really matters is the quality of management. Just what this means is difficult to define. **Most successful egg producers are convinced that what counts is constant attention to detail by a conscientious attendant.** This is most necessary in the early days of brooding and whenever some change is made in the environment of the bird, as happens when it is moved from stage to stage in the rearing programme.

Chicks have habits and instincts. Unfortunately, it is not always possible for their behaviour to be reasonable because to economise on labour and capital they are usually run in very large groups. But, within these units, poultry do better in small groups—if this can be managed—and ideally housing should make provision for this. For larger farms it is suggested that 5,000-bird houses should be divided into pens for 500 to 1,000 birds; evidence suggests that even smaller units will give better results.

Each group, and preferably each house, must contain only birds of the same age and from the same source. The divisions between groups within a deep-litter or wire-floored house should be solid for the lower 3 feet, because there is some evidence this helps prevent leucosis.

Management is fundamentally an understanding of the needs of chicks reared in large groups, plus an ability to train them so that they can adapt to this situation.

As we have seen, it is common to rear pullets in a number of stages before they finally go into the laying quarters. In this case, the job of management is to see that these transfers are made without "stress" (which causes a check to growth) and, perhaps more important, without casualties.

58

Birds always do better in small groups. The aim should be about 500 birds to a group.

In the early days, a close watch must be kept on temperature, which should not drop abruptly. Where the temperature is correct for age and there is adequate floor space, no trouble is likely to be experienced. But real trouble occurs when birds are shifted to new quarters without having been trained to use perches (upon which they can spread out naturally), or to strange conditions where, without central light or warmth, they huddle and crowd in the corners, causing numerous casualties from crushing.

Panic and Smothering—Birds panic for many reasons, most of them unknown. But the bigger the flock, the more casualties there are from smothering. It is therefore tempting for the safe-minded investor to rear in small cages and to use laying batteries.

Apart from a move to strange surroundings, the commonest causes of smothering are unfamiliar noises, sudden cuts in lighting or an unexpected cold snap.

Sudden noises are not likely in windowless houses, which is one reason why the type is becoming increasingly popular. Training will help the birds to adjust themselves to sudden power cuts. The effects of cold snaps are also eliminated in a controlled-environment house.

The answers to crushing are, therefore: early teaching, a

59

controlled-environment house, or rearing (and laying) in small cage units. All other systems demand careful management, and the following are some useful rules:—

(1) Where applicable, always allow birds to go to roost in natural daylight. Also, alterations to the timing of artificial lighting should be made in the morning, not at night.

(2) Wire off the corners of the house. Although this helps, it is not completely foolproof.

(3) When birds are moved to new houses or range shelters, they should have dim lights or a hurricane lamp until they have settled down.

(4) When moving the birds to a new house, the main flock should be preceded a day or two before by "pathfinders" or a small advance guard. Moving the flock in two or three batches also helps.

(5) Temporary perching platforms placed in wire or slatted houses for the first week after moving also encourage the birds to settle down.

This crushing may be due to the brooder being too hot; the surround being too close; or a draught

These guards prevent birds taken off heat from crowding and crushing in the corners

Platforms and Perching—Training for perching can be done from a very early age when the Wooster brooder is used. The top of the brooder is insulated with wood shavings, which the chicks soon learn to use as a resting place. If a roosting platform is supplied at 5 weeks, the chicks quickly learn its desirability as a roosting place.

Birds soon learn to perch on top of Wooster brooders. A perching platform should cover the brooder later on.

It is common in some large rearing units to have half the house litter and the other half wire or slats. Feeders and drinkers are gradually moved from the litter to the wire or slatted area, and soon the birds spend the night there. They may be encouraged to use the platform as early as 2 weeks old, by which time they are able to eat from a mechanical feeder, often profitably used as the sole feeder on the platform. Apart from learning how to perch at an early age, there are the other advantages of keeping the droppings and spilt water beneath the platform, and not in the litter. There are of course many variations on this principle of teaching the perching habit early.

Feeding and Drinking Space—An important point in management is the provision of enough feeders and drinkers, and the proper spacing of them. As we have seen, these should be placed near the warmth of the brooder in the first few days of the chick's life. Thereafter they should be

61

INCREASE EGG PRODUCTION

PAULS

By Appointment to
H.M. Queen Elizabeth II
Manufacturers of
Animal Feeding Stuffs

LAYING FOODS

The Sign of Scientific Feeding

R & W PAUL LTD

Mills at London, Ipswich, Avonmouth, Manchester, Hull, King's Lynn, Faversham

gradually placed farther away. But at no time, not even when they are adult, should birds have to walk more than 10 feet for water, or 12 to 15 feet for feed. Some producers set the equipment at greater distances, but the number of culls they get tells whether they are doing it successfully or not. Birds like to keep to their own little group, in its own restricted locality.

There is plenty of trough space here. But note the corners (in which the birds can huddle), and the broken surround, which has trapped a bird.

Feeding space should be 1½ to 2 in. for 100 birds, rising to 5 to 6 in., or 4 tube feeders, at point-of-lay. For drinkers, allow one for 100 birds or, with the double-balanced pan type, 7 for 1,000 birds. Automatic feeders can be used by birds from 2 to 3 weeks onwards, and 5,000 birds reared at a time would justify automatic feeding. Feeders and drinkers should, as far as possible, be of the same type as those used in the laying house.

63

Labour Needs—Since close attention is needed for very young birds—indeed for growers of all ages—it is obvious there is a limit to the number of birds that can be placed in the hands of one man. But a reasonable figure to work on is $2\frac{1}{2}$ to 3 man-minutes per day per hundred birds. Doing the routine work only, a man can cope with up to 10,000 birds, but doing all the work he could manage only 6,000. (These figures apply to intensive rearing.) It is doubtful if a man could manage so many in, for example, haybox brooders. Work is particularly heavy when chicks are transferred to them, for each brooder holds only 40 chicks at the most. And, until they have settled down, a primitive form of heat and light in the form of a hurricane lamp is necessary in each brooder. This obviously limits the number that can be looked after.

Range shelters also demand close attention for a few days after the birds have been moved to them. A light is necessary, as well as the presence of the attendant, to see that each shelter is not overcrowded.

A close watch must also be kept on lighting in intensive houses. The actual amount required for merely finding a way about the house is not very great, but the light should be well distributed. In particular, the corners should be well lit, for it is dark corners that encourage crowding on the slightest pretext and produce casualties. Management must therefore see that all lights are working each day. When a light pattern is in use to delay maturity, it is doubly important to see that all the lights are working and the time switch properly set.

To meet all purposes, a number of small-wattage bulbs are better than a few of large wattage. A lighting intensity of 3 foot-candles can do no harm; that is equivalent to $\frac{1}{4}$ watt to a square foot, from bulbs hung about 7 feet from the floor.

Feather Picking—A problem that will certainly arise at some time or other is feather picking. It is often said that bad management is responsible for this behaviour, which often turns to the evil of cannibalism. Where there are no obvious errors of management it is more likely that it arises from strain characteristics. Some strains are vicious and some are docile. Breeders are well aware of this—hence the greater docility of the most recent high-laying strains.

But the management factors that lead to a pre-disposition to feather pecking are overcrowding, too much light (especially daylight in intensive houses), and bad spacing of feeders and waterers. All kinds of cures have been suggested, but they are not worth much as a general rule. Some rearers find it is better to de-beak as a matter of routine.

Unless one is expert, always ask the chick producer's advice on de-beaking.

There are many opinions on when de-beaking should be carried out. Sometimes it is done at day-old, in which case it must be done again before the birds go into laying quarters—perhaps earlier. Much depends on how it is done. A very severe method involves cutting sharply back the top and bottom mandibles—both at an angle so that it is difficult for the bird to grip the feather of a passing enemy and yet is able to eat food, even mash, efficiently. This is a method for those who are both brave and expert, because it could lead to uncontrollable bleeding and considerable mortality.

Probably the best method is to cut back the top mandible to as near the base of the nostril as possible, without causing bleeding of a kind that cannot be dealt with at once by the cauterising effect of the "knife". The farther back it is possible to cut, the less frequent will the need be for the operation. But, to repeat, skill is needed if trouble is to be avoided. Therefore, consult the chick supplier before embarking on what could be a bloody operation.

65

MANAGING THE HOUSE

The points given below cover the first 14 days of the chick's life—always a critical period. But the same care and attention should be given throughout rearing. Given good management and feeding, and freedom from disease and death by crowding or crushing, the birds should develop their natural capacity as layers.

Everything is as it should be in this brooder house.

Preparing for the Chicks

(1) Test all electrical and heating equipment.

(2) Spread litter to an average depth of 6 in. on an earth floor, and 3 in. on a concrete floor. One ton of shavings will cover 1,000 sq. ft. to a depth of 6 in.

(3) Switch on brooding equipment 2 days before chicks arrive. The thermostat should be regulated to give a temperature of 95 degrees F., 2 in. above the litter at the edge of the canopy.

(4) Place an 18-in. high surround 2 ft. away from the hover.

(5) Close fan openings and air inlets to maintain the house temperature at 70 degrees F.

A Few Hours Before Arrival

(1) Lay out chick-box lids or egg trays evenly around the brooder. Ten 50-chick box lids with the holes covered over will be sufficient for 1,000 chicks. Cover the trays with mash or crumbs.

(2) Set out drinkers with fresh, clean water and intersperse them between the feed trays; the chill will thus be off the water. Ten 7-lb. jam-jar type drinkers are sufficient for 1,000 chicks, or use 1-gallon type chick fountains.

(3) Switch on full white light.

When the Chicks Arrive

(1) Unbox rapidly to avoid over-heating.

(2) Watch the chicks' behaviour after a short period of settling down. If they are cold they will huddle under the hover; if too hot they will remain outside the brooder. Fans will not be necessary unless the weather is very warm and the house poorly insulated. **67**

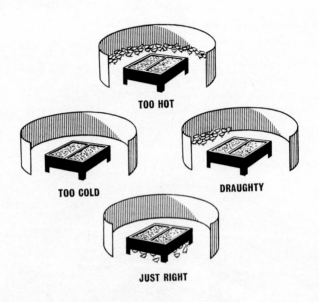

TOO HOT

TOO COLD   **DRAUGHTY**

JUST RIGHT

(3) Kill weaklings on arrival. Arrange for a post-mortem if losses exceed 1 to $1\frac{1}{2}$ per cent.

(4) Never leave brooder house doors open. Open and close doors quickly and infrequently to avoid draughts and lowering the house temperature.

Four Days Old

(1) Place some tube feeders, if used, on the ground inside the surround; if possible, dispense with the tube part. Fill the tray with mash or crumbs.

(2) Scatter a little baby-size flint grit on top of the feed. One handful is enough for 1,000 chicks.

(3) Move the surround 1 ft. to 2 ft. back from the hover and give automatic drinkers—one to every 250 chicks. Place them on boards or lay stiff paper on each side of the "U" section drinker to avoid damp litter; alternatively, the drinkers may be placed on low wire frames. But none of these methods is completely foolproof, so remove any damp litter.

(4) Do not remove the water founts until the automatic drinkers are in full use.

One Week Old

(1) Watch for feather picking, and reduce the intensity of white light if necessary. This will not upset the light patterns for control of maturity unless the lighting is made very dim.

(2) Begin switching the lights on and off in the mornings to accustom the chicks to sudden darkness; this will train them for possible power cuts which, if the birds are not prepared, may cause crowding and panicking. By 2 weeks they should be accustomed to $\frac{1}{2}$ hour of darkness.

(3) Reduce the brooder temperature by 5 degrees F., and repeat this weekly until brooding is completed.

(4) Take away the surrounds from each brooder and make one big surround to hold the chicks away from the sides and ends of the house.

(5) Use more tube feeders, and remove half the food trays and half the water founts.

Fourteen Days Old

(1) Switch on the fans and set the thermostats at 70 degrees F.

(2) Adjust inlets according to weather conditions and to balance extraction rate.

(3) Place a handful of grit in the top of each tube feeder. Repeat once a week for the rest of the growing period.

(4) Reduce brooder temperature by approximately 5 degrees F.

(5) Raise feeders and drinkers so that the lips come in line with the backs of the chicks; this reduces spillage.

(6) If there is a central roosting platform with automatic feeding, place "ladders" in position and start automatic feeding.

DELAYING MATURITY

The use of artificial lighting in poultry keeping is not new, and in the 1920's lights were used to increase winter egg production. But in the last 10 years three important changes in British poultry keeping have led to important changes in lighting techniques.

Firstly, the number of pullets hatched outside the traditional spring season has steadily increased. Secondly, although the majority of pullets are still reared on range, there are now many large units where all rearing is intensive. Thirdly, windowless housing has enormously increased the scope and the problems in using special light patterns on growing and laying birds.

Season of Hatch—When birds are reared by natural daylight, the date of hatch has a marked effect on the age at which the bird lays its first egg. Pullets hatched from November to January come into lay about 3 weeks earlier than birds of the same strain hatched in April or September.

But it is not a good thing for pullets to lay too early, because they lay small eggs for many months and, in the long run, they do not lay more eggs. Also they tend to suffer more from prolapse of the oviduct.

Experimental work at Reading University shows that early maturity in winter-hatched pullets is caused by the pattern of natural "daylength" experienced throughout their growing life. Since the length of the day is always increasing for a January-hatched pullet, she rushes into lay before she is really ready. But, once the cause of the trouble is known, the remedy is simple. Artificial lights can eliminate or reverse the pattern of light experienced by a winter-hatched bird, and make her come into lay as though she had been hatched in March or June.

Step-down Rearing—For winter-hatched birds, the recommended procedure is to give a total of 23 hours light each day for the first week of the chick's life, then reduce the day-length by equal weekly steps so that by 17 to 18 weeks of age the flock is only getting natural daylight. (See opposite.) The actual rate of decrease varies with the date of hatch: about 30 minutes weekly for November hatches, 39 minutes for December, and 25 minutes for January hatches.

Light patterns for use in conjunction with
NATURAL DAYLIGHT

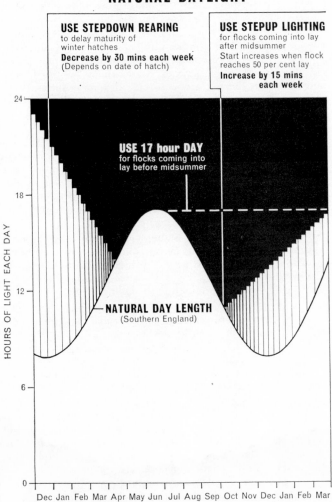

USE STEPDOWN REARING
to delay maturity of
winter hatches
Decrease by 30 mins each week
(Depends on date of hatch)

USE STEPUP LIGHTING
for flocks coming into lay
after midsummer
Start increases when flock
reaches 50 per cent lay
**Increase by 15 mins
each week**

USE 17 hour DAY
for flocks coming into
lay before midsummer

NATURAL DAY LENGTH
(Southern England)

HOURS OF LIGHT EACH DAY

24 —
18 —
12 —
6 —
0 —

Dec Jan Feb Mar Apr May Jun Jul Aug Sep Oct Nov Dec Jan Feb Mar

71

This "step-down" treatment is effective in delaying maturity, and gives larger and more eggs than can be obtained by rearing December-hatched birds by natural daylight. (Larger eggs can be a profitable factor, as shown on page 77.) The method requires some form of intensive rearing in order that artificial lighting can be used throughout the growing stage, but it does not require windowless houses.

However, the best results are not always obtained by step-down lighting. Birds coming into lay in the winter and early spring give better results than those coming into production in the long days of summer. Experiments in the U.S.A. indicate that there is an advantage in having birds reared so that daylength is short at the time when the birds are maturing. For certain hatch dates, this can only be achieved with windowless houses.

Stimu-lighting—Professor Dale King of the Alabama Polytechnic Institute in the U.S.A. has developed a system called "stimu-lighting" for use in windowless houses. The technique involves rearing pullets from day-old to 20 weeks with only six hours of light daily. From 20 weeks onwards, daylength is increased steadily at the rate of about 15 minutes each week. (See opposite.)

Stimu-lighting has given higher yields than other lighting systems, the margin in its favour sometimes being as much as 2 to 3 dozen eggs. Most of this increase is thought to be due to the short days in the growing stage, rather than to the increasing light pattern used in the laying house.

Many people are unwilling to try rearing chicks with only 6 hours of light daily, but those who have used the system report good results. Chicks do not grow as fast in the first few weeks, but they quickly make up lost ground. There is little difference in body weight at maturity, age at maturity, or egg size between a flock reared on constant short days and a flock reared on constant long days.

Step-up Lighting—The full benefits of stimu-lighting can only be obtained with windowless houses, but the lessons learned can be applied, to some extent, in ordinary laying houses with windows. Instead of using a 14-hour day throughout the winter, a system of increasing daylengths tailored to suit the particular flock is recommended.

When spring-hatched modern pullets come into lay in the autumn, production will rise to a good peak without the aid

Light patterns for use in
WINDOWLESS HOUSES

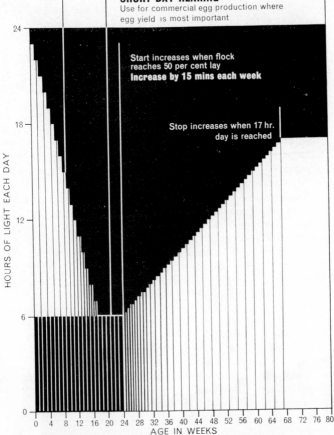

STEPDOWN REARING
Use for breeding flocks where egg size is most important
Decrease by 1 hr. each week

SHORT DAY REARING
Use for commercial egg production where
egg yield is most important

Start increases when flock
reaches 50 per cent lay
Increase by 15 mins each week

Stop increases when 17 hr.
day is reached

HOURS OF LIGHT EACH DAY

24 —

18 —

12 —

6 —

0 —

0   4   8   12   16   20   24   28   32   36   40   44   48   52   56   60   64   68   72   76   80
AGE IN WEEKS

of long, artificial days. The best method of maintaining a high rate of lay for as long as possible is to give 15 minutes more artificial light each week to increase the total daylength (natural plus artificial).

These increases should be started when the flock reaches 50 per cent production, and should be maintained until a 17-hour day is reached. Increases beyond 17 hours are not harmful, but they do not stimulate extra production and the electricity is wasted. (See last table.)

Once the bird starts to lay, a decline in daylight tends to lower egg production; if it is severe enough the bird will start to moult. The reason that pullets moult in October and November is that natural daylength declines in August and September. Neck moulting was common before the use of artificial lighting became general, and some moulting may occur even in a flock that receives a 14-hour day from mid-September onwards. The best policy for pullets already in production in June is to maintain daylength at 17 hours by using artificial lights.

Choice of Lighting System—The choice of system is not simply a matter of deciding which is best, because the facilities available vary from farm to farm. Choice also depends to some extent on the type of bird and the product to be marketed.

Winter-hatched flocks are best avoided altogether on range rearing. For those with intensive-rearing facilities, but not windowless houses, natural daylight will serve well enough for hatches between April 1 and September 30. Other hatches should be given step-down lighting in the growing stage.

If windowless rearing accomodation is available, there is a choice between step-down rearing and short-day rearing. Evidence suggests that short-day rearing is more profitable when eggs are sent to the packing station, because it gives reasonable egg size and the highest possible yield. If eggs are wanted for hatching, step-down lighting is preferred,because it gives the largest possible early egg size.

In windowless laying houses, daylength should be increased steadily from 6 hours to 17 hours when the birds reach 50 per cent production. In laying houses with windows, daylength can be increased from the time that the birds reach 50 per cent lay, adding 15 minutes each week until a 17-

hour day is being provided. When birds come into lay before midsummer, the 17-hour day must be given from June onwards.

Daylength must not be reduced if a flock is reared with natural daylight and transferred at point-of-lay to a windowless house. An abrupt change from long, natural days to a 6-hour day will cause moulting and a drop in egg production. The recommended procedure is to give pullets the same daylength in the windowless laying house as they were having naturally on range. Daylength can then be increased when a 50 per cent rate of lay is reached.

Windowless houses have many advantages apart from the opportunity to control the light pattern. However, they should be used in conjunction with windowless brooding and rearing accomodation, so that the light environment can be completely controlled at all ages.

RESTRICTED DIET TRIALS

Restricting food intake to delay maturity of early-hatched pullets is an old practice. The exact effects of this practice have been studied in a number of trials (notably in Canada), and the results of two of these trials are presented below.

Experiment 1—This experiment covered 11,000 White Leghorns on six farms. The birds were transferred to grass at 6 to 8 weeks and divided into two groups. One group was fed mash to appetite and the other was restricted to 70 per cent of that amount. At 21 weeks both groups were penned, and given *ad lib*, feed and 13 hours light to 500 days—the end of the experiment.

Results

Mortality: higher for birds reared on restricted diets; little difference during the laying period.

Egg Production: 1·1 more eggs for each bird on restricted diet.

Delay in Maturity: 12 days later in birds on restricted diet.

Egg Size at Maturity: no significant difference.

Rearing Costs: less for birds on restricted diet.

Opinions differ over delaying maturity by food restriction. In practice, it is generally easier to delay maturity by light treatments.

Experiment 2—This was a two-year test of White Leghorn production. The birds were divided into two groups: one half were fed *ad lib* the other half had a feed restriction of 37·5 per cent from 3 to 8 weeks, and 32·5 per cent from 8 to 21 weeks. Feed was not restricted during the laying period.

Results

Age of Maturity: delayed 2 weeks in the birds on restricted diet.

Rate of Lay: birds on restricted feed laid at a higher rate than the birds on *ad lib* feed, doing so until the end of the test. Following a forced moult, they came back into production more quickly and again laid at a higher rate.

Egg Size: inconclusive in the first year of production, but in the second year the birds on restricted diet laid larger eggs.

Mortality: for the birds on restricted diet it was high in the rearing period, but lower during production.

Summary—Expert opinion is divided on the value of restricted feeding for delaying sexual maturity. The natural control of sexual maturity is by decreasing daylight in the second half of the year—a delay of up to 2 weeks can be obtained this way without trouble or expense.

Early-hatched birds subjected to natural lighting (causing precocity) and under restricted feeding (causing delayed maturity), appear to be under a dual strain. This can be avoided if control is by reduced lighting only.

Some of the ill effects of restricted feeding, for instance higher mortality and unthriftiness, are due to the fact that where medication has been added to the feed at the correct rate for *ad lib* feeding, it has been insufficient for birds on restricted feeding.

DECREASING LIGHT: LARGER EGGS & LARGER CHEQUES

It does not always follow that income per bird rises with the hen-housed average. On a farm where the accounts were examined, the less productive of two flocks gave the highest net profit.

There were over 2,000 WL × RIR in each flock, and they had approximately the same early-spring hatching date. One flock was reared on grass throughout and came into lay at 16 weeks. It achieved the excellent hen-housed average of 258 eggs.

The other flock was housed in a windowless house, and given a decreasing light pattern. The birds reached 54 per cent production at 25 weeks (see table), and by year end had reached a hen-housed average of 203 eggs. But the net profit from these less-prolific producers was 7s. 6d. a bird more—**the sole reason was superior egg size.**

	25 WEEKS OLD (per cent)	47 WEEKS OLD (per cent)	67 WEEKS OLD (per cent)
PRODUCTION	54	70	56·5
LARGE EGGS	2	63	74
STANDARD EGGS	49	30	20
MEDIUM EGGS	44	1	0

FEEDING

Although much is known about feeding chicks and growers, there is a great deal still to be discovered. For instance, the whole concept that feed consumption is related to energy needs, and protein requirements are closely related to energy, is fairly recent and we must expect continuous progress to be made along lines such as this.

As new evidence becomes available, it is likely to be in the hands of the nutrition experts first, and to take some time before reaching advisors and producers. Since the first 8 weeks of the chick's life are critical, it is best to use compounds that have been formulated by those who have the latest knowledge and equipment.

The Bird's Energy Needs—Most systems of management allow free access to food for chickens of all ages and, under under these conditions, the rate of consumption is primarily determined by the energy needs of the bird. When high-energy feed is given, consumption is less than when a medium or low-energy feed is given.

However, high-energy rations for chicks and growers may cause feather pecking and picking; since the producer wants to combine satisfactory growth with easy management, a medium-energy ration should be chosen. The bird's other nutritive needs, especially protein, are directly related to energy consumption, and there can be too much or too little of these factors in the ration.

When the protein level is low, extra food will be consumed in order to get enough protein. The extra energy taken in will be deposited as fat. A ration slightly low in protein may not impair growth, but in the long run it will cause inefficient food conversion and will be expensive.

Too much protein will not affect normal growth, but the excess is costly and will be used for energy purposes without fat being deposited. The correct protein-energy balance must be achieved.

The Energy-Protein Balance—The relationship between protein and energy for growing pullets is shown in the following extract:

78

"A protein level of 20 to 21 per cent with an energy level of about 900 calories gave the best growth and feed efficiency from 0 to 8 weeks of age. Fifteen to 16 per cent protein with 800 to 1,000 calories was optimum or near optimum during the 8 to 15 week period, and 13 to 15 per cent protein with 8,000 to 1,000 calories gave the best performance with the fewest problems from feather pecking and eating during the 15 to 20 weeks period. An energy level of 1,000 calories was borderline for the feather picking problem, but gave the best feed efficiency. The best energy level within the above limits was a question of economics and not of nutrition."*

From this evidence, those who de-beak may use the higher level of energy from 8 weeks on.

Amino Acids—The protein that is used in the feed must contain the required amounts of amino acids, which are the constituent parts of protein.

The amino-acid requirements for growers are not as well known as for young chicks, but they are not as important. It is only the first 8 weeks that is the critical period. The choice of protein to give the right amino-acid content and the right ratio to the carbohydrate part of the ration is a skilled matter, and calls for the highest skill in compounding.

Minerals and Vitamins—Minerals and vitamins are almost of equal importance to protein and energy in the ration. The correct balance between minerals and vitamins and protein is shown in Table 1. (Overleaf).

Other Factors—Finally, there are unknown dietary factors. There is evidence that such unknown factors exist in dried whey, distillers' solubles, certain green foods and the by-products from fish and meat processing. These factors may not differ from each other fundamentally but, since little is known about them, compounders find it best to allow for them when compounding rations. This can be seen in Table 2, the chick ration used at the Poultry Research Centre, Edinburgh.

* *Poultry Science, May* 1961

TABLE 1 Nutrient Requirements of Chickens
(percentage or amount per lb. feed)

	CHICKS 0-8 WEEKS	GROWERS 8-18 WEEKS
CRUDE PROTEIN %	20	16
VITAMIN A POTENCY IU/g	2·66	2·66
VITAMIN D3 IU/g	0·20	0·20
RIBOFLAVIN μg/g	2·9	1·8
NICOTINIC ACID mg/g	26·6	20·0
CHOLINE μg/g	1330	
VITAMIN K μg/g	0·4	0·4
VITAMIN E μg/g	3·1	3·1
VITAMIN B12 μg/g	8·8	2·0
CALCIUM %	1·6	1·6
PHOSPHORUS %	0·8*	0·8*
CHLORIDE %	0·3	0·3
MANGANESE μg/g	55	

* Of the total, one half at least
should be present as
non-phytin phosphorus.

TABLE 2

	%	
MAIZE MEAL	29·0	
GROUND OATS	13·0	
MIDDLINGS	13·0	
BRAN	13·0	
FISH MEAL	6·5	
SOYA BEAN MEAL	2·5	
GROUNDNUT MEAL	2·5	
DRIED YEAST	5·0	
DRIED SKIM MILK	5·0	
DRIED GRASS	5·0	
LIMESTONE	1·0	
SALT	1·0	
COD LIVER OIL	2·0	
MINERAL MIXTURE	1·0	
TOTAL	**99·5**	

THE MINERAL MIXTURE	**lb.**	
IRON SULPHATE	56	
MANGANESE SULPHATE	110	
LIMESTONE FLOUR	1,427	
STEAMED BONE FLOUR	314	
COMMON SALT	336	
POTASSIUM IODIDE	1·5	
COBALT SULPHATE	1·5	
COPPER SULPHATE	34	
TOTAL	**2,280**	

Antibiotics—Although antibiotics are often included in the rations for young chicks, they are not feeds. Their function is to change the bacterial content of the digestive tract, as a result of which they have an effect on growth and increase feed efficiency.

Home-Mixed Rations—A producer can easily and accurately mix his own foods with simple and relatively inexpensive equipment. But he cannot be certain that the cereals he grows and buys have the exact protein and energy values given in text-book tables. Individual ingredients in a ration may be 10 to 15 per cent above or below the rated figures, and this can upset the entire balance of a critical ration.

No doubt excellent chicks are reared on home-mixed rations expertly made to approved formulas; one such ration that has given consistently good results is shown in Table 3. But on commercial rations chicks only eat 1s. 8d. worth of food to eight weeks, and a saving of £3 a ton by home mixing only represents 1⅔d. a chick. A suitable home-mixed ration for intensive growers, giving approximately the correct protein-to-energy ratio, is shown in Table 4.

TABLE 3

	cwt
CHICK PROT./MIN./VIT. CONCENTRATE	4
WEATINGS	5
FRESHLY GROUND MAIZE MEAL	6
MEDIUM-GROUND BARLEY MEAL	5
TOTAL	20

TABLE 4

	cwt
40% PROT./MIN./VIT. CONCENTRATE	4
FINELY GROUND OATS	4
MEDIUM-GROUND BARLEY MEAL	6
COARSELY GROUND WHEAT MEAL	5
GRASS MEAL	1
TOTAL	20

Food Supplements on Range—When the strain of bird, its rations, and the lighting patterns are known, the weight of the bird, the date of maturity, the egg size and pattern of laying can be foretold reasonably accurately. And since a greater number of laying units will be working to well-planned schedules, accuracy in feeding will be more important. But this is difficult when grass forms a part of the ration, because its quality varies considerably. In a well-designed ration, good grass will not gravely affect the balance, but poor grass is best avoided.

When supplementary cereals are fed, the producer should know what place they have in the ration. It is probable that range grass and corn supplements for growing pullets will become less popular as the emphasis on balance in feeding grows.

Amount of Feed Required—The amount of feed required for birds to reach certain live weights, and the time taken in doing so, are shown in Table 5. Figures are given for White Leghorns and for heavy breeds of chickens in general.

TABLE 5

Feed required and time taken to reach average live weights

| AV. LIVE WEIGHT | QUANTITY OF FEED REQUIRED PER BIRD (lb.) | | | |
| | WHITE LEGHORNS | | HEAVY BREEDS | |
	FEMALES	MALES	FEMALES	MALES
0·5	1·0	0·9	0·9	0·8
1·0	2·3	2·0	1·9	1·8
1·5	3·7	3·2	3·1	2·9
2·0	5·3	4·7	4·5	4·2
2·5	7·1	6·3	6·1	5·5
3·0	9·7	8·2	7·8	6·9
3·5	13·2	10·6	10·0	8·5
4·0	20·8	—	12·4	10·2

AGE TO REACH CERTAIN LIVE WEIGHTS (weeks)			
WHITE LEGHORNS		HEAVY BREEDS	
FEMALES	MALES	FEMALES	MALES
3·0	2·7	2·8	2·5
5·4	4·7	4·4	4·1
7·6	6·4	5·7	5·2
9·7	7·8	7·0	6·3
2·1	9·0	8·3	7·3
4·6	10·4	9·5	8·2
7·5	12·0	10·8	9·1
0·9	—	12·0	10·0

MASH OR CRUMBS?

Chicks and growers may be fed either mash or crumbs. Crumbs cost from 7s. 6d. a ton more to manufacture, but they have no nutritional advantage. They are made and sold because they do have the following advantages:

(1) They allow coarse, dusty or unpalatable foods to be offered in a palatable form without waste.

(2) They eliminate selective feeding. Mash tends to contain materials which differ in colour and size of particles; also, some of the more important ingredients (usually finely ground) may not be eaten in the required amounts. On the other hand, a feed of crumbs contains all the necessary ingredients in the right proportions.

(3) A meal of crumbs may be eaten in shorter time than a meal of mash and timid birds may eat all they want, even though they are unable to stay long at the trough. Weight gains are better when there is slight overcrowding; this often applies to the early days of brooding, when the brooder surrounds form a close circle to conserve heat. Broiler trials confirm higher weights and more carcass fat from feeding crumbs.

(4) No trouble arises with "bridging" when feeding crumbs. But bridging is a problem when feeding mash in tubular feeders; such feeders are popular because they allow more effective use of the floor space.

(5) The habit of picking over mash in inefficient feeders is wasteful. Crumbs are eaten by a straight pick-up, and waste is at a minimum.

(6) Crumbs retain their character and palatability for a long period. Mash quickly becomes dry and unpalatable after it has been picked over and exposed to the dry atmosphere of the average brooder. Crumbs that easily disintegrate are uneconomical, because the dust is not eaten readily.

(7) Crumbs or pellets are not blown away by the wind; often a problem with range-fed birds.

An All-Mash Ration—An all-mash ration, recommended by the Milk Marketing Board, is shown in Table 6. The ration is for feeding from 10 weeks onwards, with skim milk given *ad lib*. Given unrestricted access to skim milk, 100 birds will drink up to 5 gallons daily.

TABLE 6

	cwt
COARSELY GROUND WHEAT	$3\frac{1}{2}$
GROUND BARLEY	$3\frac{1}{2}$
MAIZE MEAL	$1\frac{1}{2}$
SUPERFINE WEATINGS	$\frac{1}{2}$
GRASS MEAL	$\frac{1}{2}$
MINERAL/VITAMIN SUPPLEMENT (approx.*)	$\frac{1}{2}$
TOTAL	10

*(or at manufacturer's recommended rates).

DISEASE

The Build-Up of Infection—Poultry farmers often find that results are outstandingly good in a new building or on new land. But in time, as batch follows batch, productivity falls and disease may increase. In many cases, this is due to the presence of an increasing number of micro-organisms (viruses, bacteria and parasites), which are capable of causing disease if present in large enough numbers. The term commonly used for such situations is a "build-up" of infection.

Many of these micro-organisms (such as a few worm eggs or *E. Coli* bacteria) cause little harm if they are present in small numbers, and they can be considered as normal inhabitants of the chickens. But, if they build up in the soil and the house, they will eventually invade the body in large numbers and disease will occur. Unfortunately, the occurrence may be slow and preceded by a period of poor results that cannot be traced to a definite cause. The root cause is thus missed, and tremendous losses occur without the nature of the losses being apparent.

The dangers of a build-up of infection are greatest for young stock. Day-olds are the most vulnerable, and adult birds the least. The danger also appears to be proportionately greater with the size of the unit and with rates of stocking—physically, this is not difficult to understand.

The most serious carriers of disease, once the build-up has occurred, are the birds themselves. This is why a period of de-population is essential.

De-population goes hand-in-hand with resting, cleaning and disinfection in eliminating or preventing a build-up of infection.

Preventing Build-Up— The procedure is to empty the site of poultry, clear all litter from the buildings and take it as far from the buildings as possible. All utensils and any part of the building caked with droppings should then be cleaned. Many bacterial spores, parasites and viruses can live for months (in some cases years) if protected by

Disease problems multiply when birds are confined in large numbers and in restricted space. The more space, the less chance there is of infection.

organic matter. In the same way, they can also resist many disinfectants, which is why cleaning before disinfection is so important.

It helps cleaning problems if the inside surfaces of buildings are smooth and tough. Good materials are asbestos, cement, plywood or metal lining. Rafters and purlins should be placed behind the inside cladding. A concrete floor is invaluable, and any rearing house that is in constant use should have one. It is most difficult to check the build-up of disease in earth, and *E. Coli* and parasitic infections can

89

become serious in such circumstances. A useful tip with earth floors is to disinfect the floor by soaking, then lay polythene or kraft paper before putting down the litter for the next crop.

Inside the house, good use can be made of Formalin and Chloroxylene/Triethylene Glycol mixtures as aerosol fumigants and disinfectants. Land is best rested for at least 6 months, and cultivated, or stocked with a different species of livestock.

Once the full treatment has been correctly given it is theoretically possible to re-stock at once. However, most buildings are made so that such treatment is not completely effective, and a rest period of 3 to 4 weeks is safer.

The interiors of intensive houses must be clean and smooth to make washing-down and disinfection easy.

DISEASES AFFECTING CHICKS AND GROWERS

BIRDS ON LITTER

Aspergillosis—This disease is caused by a fungus that multiplies in the lungs and air sacs. The condition stems from mouldy, musty litter. High mortality can occur with young chicks; with older birds the disease is generally chronic. There is no effective treatment.

Coccidiosis—Coccidiosis is discussed on page 94.

Worms—Worms are common with damp, earth floors and litter. The symptoms are listlessness, anaemia and many culls. The cure is to use piperazine compounds in the feed or water for 24 hours, and repeat 3 to 4 weeks later.

BIRDS ON GRASS

Impaction of Crop and Gizzard—This condition is caused by grass or fibrous material. Sometimes many birds on grass are affected and appear debilitated. Keeping the grass short and fresh is an obvious precaution. Often other dietary factors are to blame, and the condition sometimes follows a setback.

Round Worms—Attacks of round worms are likely to occur when arks and range shelters are not moved frequently and damp patches occur around drinking vessels.

BIRDS ON WIRE FLOORS

Septic Arthritis—Septic arthritis leads to lameness, which is caused by the swelling of joints, legs and feet. The infective organism is a staphylococcus, entering the body through cuts and wounds. The condition can be treated by antibiotics if it is seen in time.

Many people have noted that the small "growths" on wire mesh caused by poor galvanising are a frequent cause of this complaint. Removing these by filing, or substituting plain wire has helped the problem.

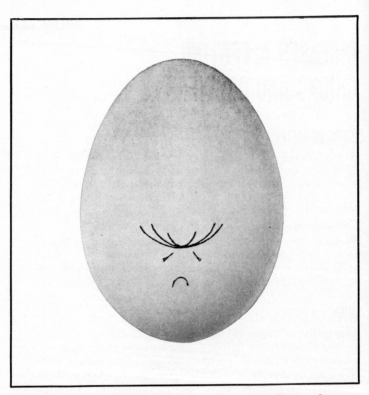

Don't let stress get your profits down

Feed High Level Terramycin—the broad spectrum antibiotic with the potency-protected molecule—to overcome stress and boost egg production safely. Feed High Level Terramycin under the guidance of your veterinary surgeon or practitioner to keep both laying and egg profits at a healthy level.

HIGH LEVEL **TERRAMYCIN** *

ANTIBIOTIC FEED SUPPLEMENT

 PFIZER LIMITED, SANDWICH, KENT.   * Trade Mark

10369

BIRDS IN INTENSIVE HOUSES

Coli Septicaemia (E. Coli)—These bacteria are normal inhabitants of poultry intestines. However, under broiler or highly-intensive systems there is some loss of condition and some mortality. Over-crowding and faulty ventilation are the commonest causes.

Diagnosis is difficult, but the main symptoms are similar to those of respiratory diseases.

Chronic Respiratory Disease—This disease is associated with infectious bronchitis. In the condition, chicks are dejected and poor doers. The cause is believed to be a pleuro-pneumonia organism. Outbreaks extend over a long period and, although there are few deaths, there are many culls.

The symptoms are like many other diseases in which respiratory trouble is apparent, such as Fowl Pest. The vet should be called whenever there are any signs of loss of condition, noisy breathing, coughing, etc.

Generators are available that can thoroughly disinfect a large house in a few minutes at relatively low cost.

COMMON POULTRY DISEASES

Coccidiosis—Coccidiosis is probably the most common disease of growing poultry, and the second most common disease of adult poultry. These assumptions are based on work at the Poultry Research Station at Houghton, Hunts; as is the rest of this discussion on coccidiosis. Coccidiosis occurs in two forms: caecal and intestinal.

Caecal Coccidiosis—This condition is not common in older fowl because most of them will have acquired a resistance to the disease from exposure to *E. Tenella* as chicks. However, it does occur in growers and layers, so anti-coccidial drugs for older fowl should be active against *E. Tenella* as well.

Intestinal Coccidiosis—The various forms of intestinal coccidiosis are the more usual disease in older birds. The reason for this is that the species of coccidia responsible for them either produce fewer oocysts than *E. Tenella* over a given period, or are less virulent than *E. Tenella*. Therefore, more of their oocysts must accumulate before disease-producing levels are reached.

One intestinal disease in fowl is associated with *E. Necatrix* which, in heavy infections, causes severe damage to the wall of the upper small intestine, and often ends fatally. Another intestinal disease is associated with *E. Acervulina*, a parasite of the small intestine, where it may inflict superficial damage to the lining. Heavy infestations of *E. Acervulina* affect weight gain and egg production, and may be fatal.

Another intestinal disease is associated with *E. Maxima*. When this species is present in large enough numbers it may cause considerable damage to the lining of the middle part of the small intestine. This again affects weight gain and probably egg production, and may be fatal.

The species *E. Brunetti* has been known for some years in the U.S.A. and is now in this country. It affects the lower small intestine and caeca. Sulphonamides are reported as being useful in curtailing established outbreaks.

Coccidiostats—It should be stated here that coccidiostats may not be the complete solution to coccidiosis, because species of coccidia do not respond equally well to the same drug, neither do strains of the same species obtained from

94

different locations. Fortunately, there may soon be single drugs that have control over at least some strains of each species.

In general, Amprolium and Zoalene give more reliable control of both caecal and intestinal (*E. Necatrix*) coccidiosis than some other drugs. Other drugs may give greater control of *E. Acervulina* and *E. Maxima*. Although the drug Nicarbazin is effective against *E. Acervulina* and *E. Maxima*, it cannot be used around the time of lay, when both species may be troublesome, for it has side-effects on the quality of the egg.

The following table sets out the anti-coccidial drugs to use against various strains of coccidiosis:

	PREVENTIVE MEDICATION	CURATIVE MEDICATION	
Caecal coccidiosis (Eimeria tenella)	Amprolium Nicarbazin Nitrofurazone Zoalene	Sulphamethazine Sulphaquinoxaline	
Intestinal Coccidiosis (Eimeria necatrix)	Amprolium Nicarbazin Nitrofurazone Zoalene	Bifuran Nitrofurazone	against some strains of E. necatrix
		Sulphamezathine Sulphaquinoxaline	against some strains of E. necatrix
Eimeria acervulina	Amprolium Nicarbazin	Sulphamezathine Sulphaquinoxaline	
Eimeria maxima	Zoalene	Sulphamezathine Sulphaquinoxaline	

Note: Instructions for dosage of drugs are supplied by the manufacturers and must be strictly followed.

95

Coccidiostats may also fail to control disease under various circumstances. For instance, when birds are sick they may eat less than usual and so take in less of a medicated food. Also, a sickness may be caused by some disease which coccidiostats do not control, and the primary disease may be obscured by the secondary development of coccidiosis.

Management—The level of infection to which the birds are exposed should be reduced by good hygiene and by preventive medication. One of the most important precautions to take is to keep the house dry.

Early diagnosis is important, because the disease may spread rapidly through a flock. Examination of a few diseased birds by a diagnostic laboratory will tell the poultryman what he has to guard against in the rest of his flock.

Fowl Paralysis and Leucosis—Fowl paralysis is usually revealed by paralysis of legs, wings or neck. The bird is unable to stand, and its physical condition gets progressively worse. Leucosis is shown by wasting; a post mortem often reveals an enlargement of the liver, spleen and kidneys.

POWERFUME

The **POWERFUME** electric fumigator has created a landmark in the disinfestation and sterilization of poultry houses. It is now an essential piece of equipment for all progressive poultry farmers. Up to 40,000 cubic feet can be fumigated in one operation.

For further details and/or **FREE** *demonstration, please write to:*

POWER FUMIGANTS LTD.
3 London Wall Buildings,
London, E.C.2

The probable cause of both these diseases is a virus; older birds may be the carriers. There is no cure, although some strains are resistant and should be selected. Additionally, there is hope that vaccination will eventually be possible. Regarding measures now, there should be at least 100 yards separation between young and old stock, and where possible separate attendants for young and adult stock.

Fowl Pest—The diagnosis of Fowl Pest is difficult, but the signs to look for are any respiratory abnormality, and nervous disorder such as coughing, sneezing, colds, and paralysis of the neck, wings or legs; other symptoms are loss of appetite, yellowish-green diarrhoea and ruffled feathers. **Any signs like these should be reported immediately.**

A scheme for vaccination against Fowl Pest has been started by the Ministry, with poultrykeepers responsible for the vaccinating.

Generally the first vaccination is at 3 weeks of age, and one vaccination should be sufficient for broilers. Laying pullets will require a second vaccination before coming into lay, and again between each laying period.

Immunity is provided about 10 to 20 days after vaccination. A satisfactorily vaccinated hen will normally pass immunity on to her progeny, protecting them for about their first 3 weeks.

Epidemic Tremors—Birds affected with epidemic tremors are dull and reluctant to move. When they do move there is inco-ordination and often tremors of the head and neck. Outbreaks are spasmodic and are caused by a virus, which is possibly inherited. There is no cure, and mortality is around 5 to 15 per cent.

Infectious Synovitis—This is a disease of growing birds. The symptoms are a pale comb, lameness and retarded growth. Later the comb shrinks and swellings occur around the joints and breast; discoloured droppings are often seen. Mortality is around 10 per cent.

The disease is slow spreading, and direct contact is necessary for its transmission. High-level antibiotics have been used against the disease with some success.

CONTRACT REARING

Contract rearing is an attempt to stabilize the marketing of a highly-speculative article, and to ensure a controlled supply of first-quality pullets. The term "contract rearing" implies some form of legal agreement between the rearer and the purchaser regarding a batch of pullets. The form of contract ranges from a word-of-mouth agreement between neighbours, to the legally-prepared document of the large egg group, signed by all the participating parties.

However, signing a document does not guarantee freedom from the pitfalls of poultry rearing. When things such as shortage of numbers or poor-quality birds do occur, it is seldom that legal action is resorted to.

If this is so, are contracts necessary and what purpose do they have? Certainly some form of contract is necessary, even if it is only an exchange of letters stating such essentials as so many birds of a certain type, grown to a certain age, to be sold at a certain price.

Group contracts are usually more comprehensive, stating responsibility for carriage, de-beaking and worming; and the position regarding the inclusion of extra pullets. Should there be any complaints, the group appoints an arbitrator, whose decision regarding the complaint will be abided by. It is his task to decide whether the pullets are up to standard and whether an adjustment in price is necessary; if the pullets are sufficiently poor, he may decide to decline delivery.

This point is one of the strengths of group contracting. Should a batch of birds be rejected, the group will have the facilities to organise quickly an alternative source, and thus avoid the producer's laying house being empty.

The better organised groups generally have a fieldman administering the scheme and supervising the rearing of the pullets. Should trouble arise in any particular batch, the group and the prospective buyer are warned and can take remedial action. It is not certain that the group could help the man rearing the faulty batch, but in any case he is no worse off than if he were not under a group contract.

Past Errors—When organised contract rearing was being started in Britain in 1959, some errors were made. The chief of these was too rigid control by the group over the chick, feed and housing. It was soon discovered that although farmers were keen to organise their egg and pullet production, there was a limit to how much dictation they would tolerate.

Present Conditions—Present-day contracts therefore are wider in scope and, provided the pullet produces good-quality eggs, the chick, feed and housing are not narrowly stipulated. Some egg groups are possibly unwisely influenced in their choice of chick, feed and house (items usually bought by the individual through the group) by the amount of discount offered by the various suppliers.

Another factor in contract rearing is that the buyer usually stipulates what sort of article he wants; for instance, a certain bird, at a certain age, reared by a certain method. This is not always an advantage to the rearer, and the prospective rearer must be certain of what is involved in any contract before he agrees to it.

It is likely that the contracting systems operated by the groups owning packing stations (with sound retail or whole-sale outlets) are the ones that will succeed. This is of particular benefit to the rearer who deals in thousands of birds each year. These groups have had a significant effect in pullet rearing—they have brought the price of pullets down sharply over the last 18 months.

The usual price before this period was between 18s. and 20s. for a 16-week old pullet. Present-day prices for the same bird are around 14s. to 16s. To many people this is dangerously near the level where skimping on rearing costs is liable to be encouraged—with the detrimental effect on the pullet showing up in the laying house.

Can 15s. for a 16-week old pullet give a reasonable return in capital investment? **The answer is "Yes", provided the rearing is run as a business and not as a farming side-line.**

Before examining the economics of rearing, it is essential to bear in mind that facts and figures do not indicate the quality of the pullets produced. Unless high quality can be maintained, there will be no continuity of orders. And continuity is essential, because failure to keep the rearing house filled to capacity will lead to irregularity of income and reduced profits.

Rearing Costs—At a selling price of 15s., profit per bird will be relatively small. High income will only come from regular throughput and the production of at least 95 per cent saleable pullets.

The estimated cost of rearing, with the percentage of total cost, is as follows:

	s.	d.	%
COST OF CHICK	3	6	28
COST OF FEED	7	0	56
OTHER CHARGES	2	0	16
TOTAL	12	6	100%

Price of Chick—The price of 3s. 6d. is based on a buying price of £17 10s. for 100 day-olds. This is an average of advertised prices; one difference is that some companies provide 2 per cent extra chicks.

Price of Feed—The figure of 7s. can probably be bettered, because it equals 18 lb. of feed per bird at 4d. per lb.; or £37 per ton. With intensive rearing the smaller hybrid would probably eat less than 18 lb., but under those conditions quality becomes extremely important, and quality costs money. Intensive rearing usually implies a restricted-light programme which, although it can restrict feed consumption and lower the feed bill, does so to the apparent detriment of the pullet. It may appear a little backward, although its ultimate performance may be better.

Other Charges—"Other Charges" include labour, depreciation on house and stock, shavings, medicaments, electricity and water; labour and depreciation are the most important items. Labour charges depend on the system employed; on the basis of one man for 10,000 birds, labour will cost 5d. a bird. It is doubtful if a man (at £14 for 18 weeks) will be fully employed but, unless he can be usefully employed elsewhere, the rearing must carry the full cost.

The house and equipment will cost around 2s. 6d. per square foot. If each bird is given 1½ to 2 sq. ft., the charge will be 10 per cent of 20s. = 2s. If 2½ batches are put through each year, the annual charge per bird will be 2/5ths of 2s. = 10d. per bird depreciation on house and equipment.

Mortality Charges—The depreciation on the stock depends on mortality. If there is a 10 per cent mortality or wastage (including sexing errors), the survivors must bear a cost of just over 1d. That assumes the wastage is in the first few days when the only charge is the chick price. An outbreak of coccidiosis, with 5 per cent mortality at 10 weeks of age, would cost approximately the same amount.

The main miscellaneous charges can therefore be around 1s. 7d.; to which brooding cost (2d.) and litter (1d.) have to be added.

Accepting the cost of 12s. 6d. per pullet as being attainable, what sort of business has one got? For an outlay on fixed capital of 20s. per bird, there will be a profit of 2s. 6d. (15s. less 12s. 6d.). Allowing 2 weeks between batches, the yearly return is 2s. 6d. × 2½ = 6s. 3d. As there is no sale until the end of the crop, and assuming no credit facilities, the investment return is 6s. 3d. on 32s. 6d. (20s. + 12s. 6d.), or 19 per cent.

The Risk—This is an attractive return, but livestock are involved, which always increases the risk of the investment. An outbreak of disease, forcing the premises to close, or failure to dispose of a batch of pullets at the proper time, will make a drastic alteration to the investment return. Obviously, rearing on contract will insure against some of these snags.

There are some rearers who ask—and get—20s. for a point-of-lay pullet (18 to 22 weeks), and 18s. for a 16-week old. In most cases the reason for this is that the pullets have a reputation as first-class layers. Such rearers do not need to worry about group contract rearing, although most of them have their production planned so that few pullets are started

SAVE
2d A DOZEN

— off your feeding costs!

No catchpenny claim, but the evidence of extended trials by independent egg producers co-operating with Lever's. Different crosses and hybrids were tested under varying intensive conditions. Over 9 months, the average cost of producing a dozen eggs on Lever's Super Layers Mini-Pellets or Meal was 2.1 pence less than on ordinary battery food. **The average profit per bird was 3/1d. higher.** Rate of lay was almost 4% more, food per dozen nearly 11% less. With larger eggs and longer lays as well, egg producers everywhere are piling up proof positive that Lever's Super Layers gives EXTRA PROFIT—EVERY TIME.

Lever's
SUPER LAYERS
supersedes all others

CONTACT YOUR LOCAL LEVER'S MAN FOR FULL *FACTUAL* INFORMATION

L.C.F.A. 828

on speculation but are sold in advance; often a 10 per cent deposit is asked at the time of starting the chicks.

The Group and the Rearer—Many contracts stipulate the conditions of rearing in order to ensure that disease is kept to a minimum. Provided the administration of the group is sound, then approved rearers can be selected not only on their reputation, but also on the type of housing they use.

The sensible group or prospective buyer will see that the pullets are reared away from adults, are not over-crowded, are fed on first-quality feed, and are subjected to a mutually-agreed light programme. Whatever system of rearing is employed, care should be taken to see that the birds suffer no stress when they go to their laying quarters. The birds should be vaccinated against Fowl Pest at 3 weeks old and again at time of delivery.

Any group member who is buying pullets ought to know which group rearer is going to rear his birds, and he should satisfy himself that the conditions are satisfactory. One of the problems of group contracts up to now has been the scarcity of rearers capable of rearing quality pullets. Some rearers have more money than experience and have been attracted by the guaranteed group market. Even with supervision, it takes some time for them to acquire the experience necessary to produce first-class birds.

One of the most experienced poultrymen in the country, and one who has had considerable experience of contract rearing—both as a rearer and a director of West Cumberland Farmers, a large-scale egg group—is Mr. Richard Leeming who has developed one of the most efficient rearing systems in Britain. His methods are described on page 117 of this book.

Such up-to-date conditions are not necessary to produce good-quality stock with any degree of certainty, but they do combine all the necessary factors: stock sense, well-designed buildings, and one age group. These, along with good chicks and feed, will produce pullets capable of being marketed with all the benefits of contract rearing.

REPORT ON EIGHT FARMS

INTENSIVE/RANGE REARING

Mr. C. S. Crawley is a specialist rearer of 16-week-old pullets—but with a difference. His pullet raising is integrated with general farming at Little Dene, Glynde, Lewes, Sussex, and is directed at getting a turnover of £17,000 with minimum labour (a manager and one man) and minimum capital expenditure on 85 acres.

Beef and pullet rearing go well together. Hereford × Shorthorn cows and followers keep the grass short enough for pullets to come behind, and the increased fertility grows wheat without using any nitrogen and half the normal amounts of phosphate and potash. In this way, fertiliser costs are reduced by £3 an acre.

The birds are on range from 8 to 16 weeks in range shelters. Annual throughput is 17,000. Feeding is two parts mash to one of wheat, the grain being increased as the birds get older. Their condition and stamina is shown by the fact that in cages, according to one consistent buyer, the hen-housed average is 250 eggs, with a mortality of 12 per cent.

Mr. Crawley's growers, reared in range shelters following litter, perform excellently in batteries. Mortality during lay is about 12%.

The birds are hybrids supplied by a single hatchery.

Rearing on grass frequently falls down because the grass is not kept short and in good condition—but on Mr. Crawley's farm the management is properly planned. Also, range shelters must be moved on regularly to avoid coccidiosis and worms—this is done once a week at Little Dene.

There are 27 shelters, each costing £15 to make, using farm labour. Water is provided by sheep troughs fitted with ball-cocks, fed by polythene tubing from stand-pipes in each field.

Many thousands of chicks have passed through this simple litter house, which has limited insulation.

Initially, grass was used for the 3 to 8-week stage, but hay-boxes were inconvenient and labour-consuming. Therefore, a 70 ft. × 40 ft. commercial brooder house was erected to take chicks from day-old to 8 weeks. This cost £1,800 including all brooders, feeders and drinkers, and it is a simple type compared with many broiler-type pullet-rearing houses. But the mortality rate from day-old to 16 weeks is only 4 per cent.

Insulation for the asbestos-sheet roof is partly Celotex and partly bituminised paper, suspended on strained galvanised wire. Hopper-type windows are fitted.

There may be two objections to this set-up, according to modern theory. One is the possibility of deaths from crushing on transfer from the brooder house to range shelters. But this has been taken care of by teaching the birds to **105** perch from an early age in the brooder house, by placing a hurricane lamp in the range shelters for a few nights after the move, and by watchfulness during and immediately after the move.

The other objection is that it is not possible to apply light patterns for control of age of maturity to early-hatched birds reared on this system.

Litter must be kept dry, to keep coccidiosis at bay. A drain beneath drinkers on wire platforms helps the problem.

100,000 LAYERS ON RANGE

Ten miles north of Lincoln, at Glenworth, Nr. Gainsborough, Mr. Frank Arden has one of the largest farming enterprises in England. His partner and manager, Mr. Stanley Fowler is in charge of the poultry unit, consisting of 100,000 laying pullets. And there are plans to treble this figure within the next 2 years.

All replacement pullets are reared on the farm (although the rearing unit is about two miles away from the laying unit), and a considerable number are also reared for sale. All stock are kept outside from about 3 weeks of age onwards.

Initial brooding is done in five Nissen-type houses 80 ft. × 18 ft., lined with hardboard, with 2 in. of fibreglass between the hardboard and the outer roof. Only one house is mechanically ventilated because results show that natural cross-ventilation is more satisfactory in houses of this type. The ventilating system consists of adjustable inlets down each side of the house, the stale air being extracted through cowls in the roof. There are 4 calor-gas brooders in every house, each with a capacity of 800 chicks. The chicks are confined within the brooder for the first few days by hardboard surrounds. The houses have concrete floors to ease cleaning out and to prevent build-up of disease.

At the beginning of the rearing season, approximately 1 ton of peat moss is put into each house. The litter under the brooders is removed after each batch of chicks, but the rest remains until the end of the rearing season. It is then taken out, bagged, and spread with a manure spinner.

These three-week old chicks are nearly ready to go to hay-box brooders for another 5 weeks.

At three to four-weeks old, the chicks are taken from the brooding houses and put into 330 haybox brooders made static by mounting over straw-bale walls. When the chicks are introduced into the hayboxes, a paper sack is slipped down to hang from the division of the outside and inside compartments—this prevents any draught entering from the outside compartment. The paper bags are removed and burnt after 3 days.

At eight-weeks old they go out into 150 range shelters, each holding 150 birds. In addition, there are 300 static fold units, which take 40 pullets each; droppings are removed at regular intervals.

Static hay-boxes save the labour involved in daily moving. Droppings fall through the wire floors, so reducing disease risk.

An internal feeder is necessary in range shelters, for birds must be confined when they are first transferred.

The range shelters are moved at least once a week, and gang mowers are used frequently to maintain a close, short sward. Clippings are picked up behind the gang mowers, and crop binding is virtually unknown.

Each shelter has an automatic water supply. Feeding-trough space is only sufficient for once-daily feeding. A recent introduction is an automatic pop-hole, which has been put in to a block of 11 range shelters. It was invented by Mr. Pigott of Longterton, and can be easily pre-set for any required number of birds. If set just before the evening grain feed, when all the birds come out, the pop-hole will close when the correct number of pullets are back in the shelter, and thus avoid overcrowding.

Mr. Fowler never expects to house fewer pullets than he actually pays for, with a normal hatchery supply of 2 per cent extra pullets. This is the percentage he expects to lose between day-old and housing in the laying quarters at 18 to 20 weeks of age. All pullets go into single-bird laying cages, mostly in 34,000-bird laying houses.

Although this method of rearing needs a lot of labour, very healthy pullets are produced. They can stand up to the rigours of a long and arduous laying life in a confined environment, and each pullet produces about 240 eggs in 500 days from hatch.

INTENSIVE REARING IN CAGES

To avoid wet and muddy conditions in autumn and winter, Mr. Eric Birchall of Newby Poultry Farm, Wilpshire, Blackburn, has successfully used a system of rearing birds in cages throughout the growing period.

For the first six weeks, the chicks are kept in tier brooders. Birds are normally put out at 4 weeks old from this type of brooder, but Mr. Birchall runs them on and then transfers them to the growing cages.

These cages are in a 68 ft. × 18 ft. timber house, built on brick and timber floors, which takes two blocks of double-sided cages. For every 8 ft. bay of the house there is a 2-foot square opening in the floor under each bank of cages to act as an air inlet. These inlets are covered with weldmesh or wire netting, and are baffled by a wooden plate that is controlled at the end of the house by a long strip attached to the timber shutters.

The photograph shows a floor air inlet in Mr. Birchall's house.

The air inlets, in conjunction with four 18 in. extractor fans mounted in the roof of the house, provide an air change of about 6 cu. ft. of air per bird per minute for the 2,000 birds housed in the building.

The birds are not de-beaked in the growing house, and are mash fed. The house is windowless, so light control is practised. Two houses are sited side by side and there is room between them for a manure spreader. Daily cleaning-out is thus simplified by the droppings being put through a sliding panel at the side of each house, directly into the spreader. The labour requirement for both houses is approximately 1½ hours daily.

Total cost for housing and cages for 4,000 birds was approximately £2,000. Although this may be slightly more expensive than conventional field houses or range shelters, the advantages of controlled environment far outweigh the additional cost.

The cages are normal battery ones (without the egg cradles) and measure 2½ ft. × 1½ ft. This allows roughly ½ sq. ft. floor space for each of the 8 birds in a cage.

It would be difficult to tell the difference between cage-reared pullets and others reared on range. In fact, laying results for the cage-reared pullets show that there is no loss of efficiency from confined rearing.

*The two houses have been planned
and sited to save labour.*

SINGLE-STAGE REARING ON WIRE

After abandoning attempts at outdoor rearing, Mr. David
Watkinson, of Griffin Farm, Lacock, Wiltshire, settled for
single-stage rearing. His laying unit is based on controlled-
environment houses, each containing 5,000 layers on wire.
To obtain an even and docile community, all 5,000 birds
must be reared together in a similar environment.

Mr. Watkinson had little space, and felt that full mechanisa-
tion and minimum labour was the right way to do things.
Therefore he had little doubt that single-stage rearing in a
controlled-environment was his answer. When he began,
there was little research on large-unit wire-floor rearing, so
he designed a litter house 110 ft. × 40 ft. with low eaves
(5 ft.) to avoid undue heat loss.

111

The costs of the house were:

	£
Site preparation	250
Shell and insulation	1,400
Ventilation	120
Wiring and plumbing	120
Automatic and static feeders	300
Drinkers	70
Roosting platform (added later)	100
	£2,360

Cost per bird for 5,000 birds, each allotted 1 sq. ft., was about 9s.

The 12 ft.-wide roosting platform runs the length of the house, and takes the U-shaped automatic feeding system and the automatic drinkers. Without it there was a great danger of crushing, but now brooding is done on the litter on each side of the platform.

BREEZA FANS for CONTROLLED VENTILATION *the reliable way*

Propeller fans 6″ to 30″ diameter.

Roof units 12″ to 24″ diameter.

LONDON FAN & MOTOR CO. LTD.

331, SANDYCOMBE ROAD, RICHMOND, SURREY.

Telephone: RIC: 0157

Please send me full details of BREEZA FANS for Pig and Poultry House Ventilation

Name ....

Address ....

....

FW2

Combined litter and wire floors for growers are becoming more common. Birds started on litter take readily to wire later on.

The surrounds are removed when the chicks are 2 weeks old, and small runways to the platform are placed in position. Then, with surprising speed, the chicks make full use of the platform for feeding, drinking and roosting. Since this procedure was first used there have been no deaths from crushing; the rearing mortality figure of two per cent to 21 weeks gives evidence of this. A coccidiostat is included in the feed throughout the rearing period.

Rearing costs to 21 weeks are:

						s.	d.
Feed	..	..	..	..	..	6	8
Labour	..	..	..	..	..		6
Light and heat	..	..	..	..		3
Mortality charge	..	..	..	..		$1\frac{1}{2}$
Depreciation	..	..	..	..		$5\frac{1}{2}$
Interest	..	..	..	..	..		3
						8	3

Add 3s. for the chick, and the cost to point-of-lay for the strain used comes to 11s. 3d.

Applied light patterns for the delay of maturity have given useful guidance on what is practical for large numbers reared together. Short daylengths were not satisfactory at

Griffin Farm and led to low weights at point-of-lay. A decreasing pattern, coming down to a 10-hour daylength, makes satisfactory weights, and appears to do the job of increasing egg size and preventing prolapsus.

The system is cheap and trouble-free, and emphasises that chicks must be taught or encouraged to perch early in life.

Note the Keyes trays used by Mr. Watkinson in the early stages of brooding.

Automatic feeders are a cheap investment when large numbers of birds are being reared.

WHERE THE EGGS ARE LAID TO ORDER

The first significant results achieved by Farringdon Farms Ltd. in rearing laying pullets under totally controlled conditions, are delay of first egg and reduction of mortality. The owners, Messrs. Aylward and Co., of Alton, Hampshire, set out to follow up Reading University's work on light control of the growing pullet.

They have succeeded in controlling growth rate, size and age at maturity; in increasing egg numbers (although this was not shown by Reading work), and egg size at start of lay; and in producing a more docile bird with lower mortality from the absence of stresses and checks caused by moves.

The brooder house is 200 ft. × 40 ft. and windowless. Ventilation is entirely mechanical, air being drawn in through automatically-louvred ventilators and extracted by five 24 in. fans mounted in the ridge. The ventilators are placed around the side of the house and the fans are fitted with an adjustable speed control, which can give up to 20 complete air changes an hour.

The most common form of mechanical ventilation takes air from side-wall ducts, and extracts it through the roof.

The electricity supply is arranged so that, in the event of a power failure, a bell rings in the house of the Poultry Manager, Mr. G. S. Bowles.

Insulation is very generous—corrugated asbestos, 4 in. of fibreglass, aluminium sheeting and plaster board—to give an

115

extremely low "U" value to the house, especially as it is windowless.

A great deal of attention has been given to the arrangement of lighting. There are 36, 80-watt single-tube fittings (5 feet long) arranged in three rows of 12, to give the birds $23\frac{1}{2}$ hours of light for one week.

This is decreased by one hour a week so that they have only $7\frac{1}{2}$ hours at 17-weeks old; this is continued for the next 4 to 5 weeks. Light intensity during the first two weeks is very strong to encourage activity, especially at the food and water troughs, and to give the birds a good start.

Feeders and drinkers should be well lit in the early stages of brooding, but too-intensive lighting may lead to vices.

An additional light circuit of 20 to 40 tungsten lamps comes into operation just before the main lights go out. They are then gradually put out by a motorised dimmer. Two small pilot lights with a time switch are used under each brooder to attract the chicks away from the side of the house even after the cooling-off stage. A hand-operated circuit of blue lamps enables Mr. Bowles to inspect the flock after "lights out".

The house is split into five pens, each designed to take 800 chicks, with a 2-kilowatt radiant heat brooder in each. The chicks are started on chick corn, then crumbs are introduced, and small grain is fed at 6 weeks. At 9 weeks pellet feeding begins and the grain size is increased.

The main brooder house at Farringdon Farms, Ltd., which is split into five pens, each taking 800 birds.

INTENSIVE REARING TO 16 WEEKS

Mr. Richard Leeming of Skirsgill Park, Penrith, Cumberland is a director of West Cumberland Farmers Trading Society, and also a director of the Society's egg group. All members of the group want to take advantage of orderly production and marketing, but agree that maximum production will only follow if the laying pullets are reared efficiently—to achieve this, specialist rearers have been appointed.

One of the first was Mr. Leeming, whose unit at Penrith incorporates the latest ideas in intensive rearing. The house is 175 ft. × 60 ft.; the end bay is used as a feed store, leaving just under 10,000 sq. ft. of floor for housing 8,000 pullets. They are moved at 16 weeks of age to a group producer.

The side walls of the house are of 6-in. hollow concrete blocks to a height of 3 ft., with $\frac{3}{4}$-in. tongued and grooved boarding above. This is insulated, and gives an overall height to the eaves of 7 ft.

The roof and sides, down to the blocks, consist of expanded partition board on the inside, with 1 in. of stitched-quilt fibreglass between that and the corrugated asbestos. Between the fibreglass and the insulating board, a layer of foil-backed sheeting acts as a vapour seal.

Ventilation is by five 24-in. fans in the ridge, and a 1-ft.-deep baffled slot running the full length of the side-walks just under the eaves. Air intake is controlled by a continuous slide on the outside of the house regulated by a lever and cable. Assuming the house contains 32,000 lb. weight of birds at 16 weeks of age, the ventilating system is capable of providing more than 1 cu. ft. of air per lb. of bird per minute, and the ratio of inlet to fan is 8 sq. ft. per 1,000 cu. ft. of fan capacity.

The truss supports are arranged so that a 24-ft. wide droppings pit fits exactly between them down the centre of the

Shown is the continuous slide that controls the air intake.

house. This stops 6 ft. short of the bottom end of the house to allow the attendant free access between the 18-ft. litter areas down the sides of the house.

The pit is in 12 ft. × 6 ft. sections, supported at the sides by concrete-block walls and in the middle by a row of empty oil drums. Each section is framed in 6 in. × 1½ in. timber, with 3 in. × 1½ in. braces at 2 ft. centres, and there is 1 in. sq. mesh 12-gauge ungalvanised weldmesh on the top. The litter areas are concreted, but the area under the pit is not; this has been excavated so that there is only a 1½-ft. rise on to the pit.

A central droppings pit in a basically litter house need not be very high for growers.

There are three separate circuits of 60-watt bulbs down the length of the house, which can be adjusted by means of a dimmer. This also acts as a transformer to reduce the amount of electricity consumed when the lights are dimmed.

The fans are regulated by three thermostats mounted centrally in the house—each in a separate circuit to all fans —and they are set within 5 degrees of each other. The first brings all fans on at 500 r.p.m.; the second increases this to 1,000 r.p.m.; and the third to 1,500 r.p.m. This means that the whole house is evenly ventilated.

Gas brooders are used, capable of producing 10,000 BTUs per hour. 1,000 chicks are placed under each, and are contained by a hardboard surround on the litter area.

Litter is wood shavings; a sheet of battery-cleaning paper is placed under the brooders to give the chicks a smooth surface and to avoid losses from chicks burrowing in the litter.

The paper is removed after five days with any food spilled during this period. Crumbs are fed to start with, liberally sprinkled on Keyes trays and in tubular plastic feeders with the tubes removed. Watering is by 4 sweet-jar waterers and 4 suspended plastic drinkers for each brooder.

As the chicks grow, feeding facilities are supplemented by 12 metal, tube feeders for each 1,000 birds and a double run of chain feeder on the pit. As the birds begin to use the pit, the drinkers and feeders are gradually moved over it so that most of the droppings fall into the pit. Water is gravity fed from a 250-gallon tank in the roof of the house.

The photograph shows the feed-handling arrangements on Mr. Leeming's farm.

Mash is gradually introduced and contains a coccidiostat. The feed is delivered in bulk to a timber hopper built into the feed store, then augered into a box slung from an over-head track which is used to service the tube feeders. The pullets are given plenty of light to start with, but at 3 to 4 weeks of age it is reduced to a 10-hour day and held through-out the growing period.

Mortality on a current batch of chicks is 0·5 per cent after the first week. The cost of this simple but well-planned rearing system is 10s. to 12s. per sq. ft., fully equipped.

EXTENSIVE STATIC METHOD

On Messrs. R. W. Powis and Sons' farm at Whitegates, Pilgrims Way, Harrietsham, Kent, they think that a spell outdoors provides a positive, if indefinable, effect upon growers destined for laying in an intensive house. The main plan is to rear in conventional tier brooders and cooler cages to 8 weeks, and then transfer the birds to off-th-ground, out-door shelters until they are 16 weeks old. This is now a common solution to the problem of preventing disease borne by soil and droppings.

Messrs. Powis are contract rearers as well as commercial egg producers. Their customers tend to select breeds and strains for rearing that do well in Random Sample Tests, and the Powis family like to know how these strains, reared by their methods, perform as layers. A great deal of useful information comes from these comparative observations.

Their observations are also extended to the comparative value of commercial feeds for growers and layers, and some of the results make surprising reading. They have now settled for one brand and a very limited number of strains. At best, hen-housed average is 240 eggs a year, with a mortality of 9 per cent in the laying year.

Mortality from day-old to point-of-lay is 3·4 per cent. This is mainly achieved by brooding in tier brooders at 95 deg. F., placed in an insulated room with a starting temperature of 75 deg. The cooling cages are in an adjoining room, which is given a starting temperature of 65 deg. F. The birds are finally hardened off outdoors in static shelters.

It is admitted that taking the birds outside for the final stages of rearing adds to the labour bill—which is already high because of need for scrupulous attention to disease control. The total labour cost is 1s. 6d. a bird to 16-weeks old.

Light control is not used, except for 24-hours' light for the first 4 weeks of brooding; but after this stage the growers have natural daylight. A rearer would be the first person to learn of any ill effects on early-hatched pullets from increasing daylight, but neither Messrs. Powis nor their customers seem to have any complaints.

Even during the freeze-up of 1962-3, birds housed outdoors appeared to make normal progress.

With cages, watch the height of the space through which the bird eats—if too shallow, eating is difficult; if too high, food is wasted.

The roof in this house is a corrugated asbestos 'sandwich' with 1 in. of quilt fibreglass.

REARING PULLETS FOR AN EGG GROUP

A successful pullet-rearing enterprise at Newton Arlosh, Wigton, Carlisle, is also playing its part in the integrated egg production conducted by West Cumberland Farmers Group. It is on the farm of the late Mr. R. Barnes, a pedigree breeder for many years.

A 48 ft. × 92½ ft. windowless house is used to rear 16-week-old pullets for members of the group with egg production units. Throughput is 3,000 chicks in each batch; the allowance for floor area is therefore approximately 1½ sq. ft. per bird. The side walls of the house consist of 6 in. hollow concrete blocks, cemented on the inside to give a smooth, hygienic surface. All the floor area is concreted.

The roof is a sandwich of corrugated asbestos, 1 in. thick quilt fibreglass, with a lower surface of expanded partition board, which again gives a smooth surface. Ventilation is by louvred inlets running down the side of the house, and extraction is by three 24-in. fans mounted in the roof, each controlled by a thermostat.

123

This clean interior has been achieved by using central supports, and by placing the droppings pits down the sides of the house.

To give as much clear floor area as possible, the roof trusses are supported by central steel posts, rather than the more usual double line of timber supports in a house of this width. There is a 10-ft. wide droppings-pit, 15 in. high down each side of the house. The side walls of the pit are timber, and the top is 3 in. × 1 in. ungalvanised weldmesh.

The lighting is kept to the sides of the house— over the brooders and droppings pits.

Brooding is by "Electric Hen". Mortality figures to date have averaged under 1 per cent. Lighting is by a row of incandescent bulbs down each side of the house; each alternate bulb is red-coloured to act as a dimming circuit after the bright lights are put out.

The birds are introduced to total darkness at an early age to avoid any possible upsets from power failures. Light is reduced at 3 to 4 weeks old to 10 hours per day, and kept constant until the birds are sold at 16-weeks old.

There is a 50-gallon water tank in the roof, which supplies 10 drinkers. Feeding is by a combination of automatic chain feeder and a number of small troughs.

INDEX

Designed by
Spectator Publications, Ltd., 91 St. Martin's Lane, London W.C.2

Made and printe Great Britain by
John Gardner (Printers) Limited, Hawthorne Road, Liverpool 20.